"I feel a recipe is only a theme,
which an intelligent cook can
play each time with a variation."

-Madame Benoit

© Truestar Health Inc. 2006

Published in Canada by
Truestar Press.

55 St. Clair Avenue West,
6th Floor, Toronto, ON,
M4V 2Y7

ISBN 0-9739655-2-5

Editorial Director:
Dr. Joey Shulman, DC, RNCP,
Vice President of Nutrition,
Truestar Health

Art Direction and Design:
Kaustic Design
www.kausticdesign.com

Project Manager:
Marina Phillips

Editor:
Marisa Iacobucci

Editorial Advisory Board:
Sofia Kalamaris, Chantal Richard,
Dr. David Schleich

Researchers:
Dan Gingras, Vijay Parekh,
Sarah Taylor, Barry Van Buskirk

true taste on the go

Table of Contents

Why On The Go?   5

Foreword   7

Phase 1:
METABOLIC BOOSTER PLAN   15

Phase 2:
CONTINUUM WEIGHT LOSS PLAN   47

Phase 3:
MAINTENANCE PLAN   79

Appendix A:
GLYCEMIC TABLES   111

Appendix B:
SERVING SIZES   117

Appendix C:
TRUESTAR WEIGHT LOSS PLANS   119

Why On The Go?

Let's face it, life is busy! Between picking the kids up from school, going to the gym, working at our hustle-bustle jobs and spending time with our families, down time has become a priceless commodity. Often, due to life's hectic pace, our nutritional choices become sacrificed and our health suffers. When this occurs, our energy takes a downturn, our weight can go up and our immune system takes a hit. We have all experienced the scenario of being very stressed and overloaded with work and coming down with a flu, cough or cold. This is not a coincidence — it is a result of an overloaded and poorly fed immune system.

At Truestar, the reason we have decided to release an "On The Go" recipe book is to help you make nutritional choices to keep up with your fast-paced life. A majority of the recipes you will find in *True Taste On The Go* take a mere 10 minutes or less to prepare. From quick and easy morning shakes to healthy wraps — each and every recipe will contain the perfect balance of lean protein, essential fats and low glycemic index carbohydrates to keep your energy up and your weight down. We realize life is busy and will likely stay that way. Instead of compromising on your nutritional choices, which will only slow you down even more, start eating some of our delicious "On The Go" recipes to give you some extra time and more pep in your step!

We invite you to select from a multitude of our delicious recipes designed to tempt your "On The Go" palate.

Bravo on your journey toward health and wellness and toward becoming the ultimate you. Bon appetite!

Yours in good health,

Dr. Joey Shulman, DC, RNCP,
Vice President of Nutrition, Truestar Health

FOREWORD

Hippocrates once said, "Let food be thy medicine and medicine be thy food." I could not agree with this statement more. The quality and quantity of food we eat on a daily basis have a direct impact on our health. Depending on our food choices, nutrition can be the underlying cause of various sicknesses and diseases or, alternatively, can be the springboard to a life filled with health, wellness and vigor.

Unfortunately, grocery stores are filled with processed and fake foods that are creating epidemics in our healthcare system. Consumers are ingesting harmful products such as trans-fatty acids, refined flours and sugars, preservatives, herbicides and pesticides at an alarming rate without even being aware of their health consequences. Because of this faulty nutrition, various disease processes such as type 2 diabetes, obesity, high blood pressure, cancer, depression, allergies and asthma are on the rise. In order to curb this trend, it is necessary to become informed about "what" and "how" to eat. By becoming nutritionally savvy and filling our diet with the proper amounts of carbohydrates, essential fats and lean proteins, we will be rewarded with optimal health and wellness.

THE BIG "3"

When it comes to nutrition, knowledge is power. Our mission at Truestar is to provide you with the "need-to-know" information for establishing good nutrition and permanent weight loss. All of our meal plans contain the 3 macro nutrients. This means that each meal and snack is perfectly balanced with the 3 macro-nutrients necessary for health: proteins, carbohydrates and fat. By eating in balance at every meal and snack, you will maintain hormonal balance which results in weight loss, boundless energy, improvement of mood and prevention against disease and illness. Learn more about how to eat the "good" types of carbohydrates, proteins and essential fats in the following section.

MACRONUTRIENT #1 — LOW GLYCEMIC INDEX CARBOHYDRATES

Carbohydrates are primarily found in fruits, vegetables, grains (e.g. cookies, bread, pasta, crackers) and legumes. This type of macronutrient is broken down into glucose (blood sugar) to be used as the primary source of fuel for the body. Glucose is transferred into the cells and used for energy. Certain parts of the body, such as the brain or red blood cells, can only use carbohydrates as an energy source. Other parts of the body can use other sources of fuel such as fat or protein, but none burn as efficiently and cleanly as carbohydrates.

The key to eating carbohydrates properly lies in understanding the intricate relationship between blood glucose levels and insulin. Insulin is a hormone secreted from the pancreas in response to elevated blood glucose levels. One of insulin's many roles in the body is the transport of glucose into the cells.

A scale referred to as the glycemic index measures the speed of entry of a food item into the bloodstream. The faster the speed of entry, the more insulin is secreted. Excess insulin secretion, due to the constant ingestion of high glycemic index foods, results in fatigue, weight gain, mental fogginess. It can also lead to the development of heart disease and high blood pressure.

For ranking purposes, the glycemic index is divided into 3 categories: low, medium and high. Food is categorized on a scale of 0 to 100 depending on its effect on blood sugar levels. On the glycemic scale, the highest measurement is for glucose which has the ranking of 100. For the most part, foods that are lowest on the glycemic index have the slowest rate of entry into the bloodstream and therefore have the lowest insulin response. The categories are:

Low (up to 55)
Medium (56 to 70)
High (over 70)

Another scale, called the glycemic load, is also a helpful tool to utilize in order to eat the right types of carbohydrates. The glycemic load considers the glycemic index of food as well as the amount of carbohydrates per serving. The glycemic load is the glycemic index divided by 100 and multiplied by its available carbohydrate content.

IN SUMMARY, THE VALUES ARE:

Value	Glycemic index (GI)	Glycemic Load
High	70 or more	20
Medium	56-70	11-19
Low	55 or less	10 or less

The key to eating carbohydrates properly is to consume those that are low on the glycemic index and glycemic load *(refer to Appendix A)*.

In other words:

MAXIMIZE

- vegetables such as broccoli, cauliflower, celery, cucumbers, tomatoes, spinach, peppers, eggplant, zucchini

- fruits such as raspberries, blueberries, strawberries, melon, papaya, cherries

- beans such as kidney beans, black beans, navy beans, chickpeas

- whole grains or starches in moderation; examples are slow-cooking oatmeal, kamut or spelt pasta and/or bread, brown rice, sweet potatoes or squash

MINIMIZE

- refined and processed grains such as white bread, pasta, rice and potatoes (mashed or baked white potato)

- pop, candy, cakes, cookies and other baked goods such as muffins

MACRONUTRIENT #2 – PROTEINS

Proteins are the second category of macronutrients that are a necessary part of every diet. They serve many functions in the body, such as maintaining proper growth and repair of muscles and tissues, manufacturing hormones, antibodies and enzymes and preserving the proper acid-alkali balance in the body. Proteins also trigger the release of the hormone glucagon — insulin's opposite. In other words, by eating proteins, fat loss is facilitated rather than stored. This action makes proteins a necessary component to eat at each and every meal or snack in order for weight loss and weight maintenance to occur.

MAXIMIZE:

- lean turkey or chicken breast

- fish such as salmon, tuna, mackerel, haddock, crab and lobster (once per week)

- lean beef

- egg whites and omega-3 eggs

- yogurt

- skim milk

- low-fat cottage cheese or other low-fat cheeses

- protein powder

- tofu: examples are veggie burgers, imitation ground beef, seasoned firm tofu in a stir-fry or tofu cheese

MINIMIZE:

- meats that are high in saturated fat have the potential to harm the heart when eaten in excess (Examples of high-fat meats include full-fat steak, pork, ribs and fast food options.)

- full-fat cheeses

MACRONUTRIENT #3 – FATS

Fats are a necessary part of every diet. In fact, 60% of the brain is comprised of fat! Certain fats are necessary in the daily diet for optimal energy, clarity of thought and even weight loss. To decipher the good fats from the bad, it is important to understand their critical differences.

Fats are composed of building blocks called fatty acids. There are 4 major categories of fats:

saturated fats
polyunsaturated fats
monounsaturated fats
trans fats

These categories are based on the number of hydrogen atoms in the chemical structure of a molecule of fatty acid.

Saturated fats are found mostly in animal products, dairy items (cream, whole milk) and tropical oils such as coconut, palm and palm kernel oil. The liver uses saturated fats to produce cholesterol. Excessive consumption of saturated fats can raise the level of the "bad cholesterol" known as low-density lipoprotein (LDL). Although cholesterol plays a vital role in our bodies, such as maintaining proper structure of our cell walls, production of the sex hormones estrogen and testosterone and the adrenal hormone cortisol, an increase in the amount of cholesterol we produce can also have detrimental effects on blood flow. Eating a large amount of saturated fats increases the level of LDL in our system, causing damage such as stiffening and narrowing of the arterial walls. Damage to the arterial walls increases the risk of cardiovascular disease, heart attack, stroke and other vascular disturbances. It is important to keep these fats to a minimum in the diet (approximately 5%).

Polyunsaturated fats (PUFAs) are found in most vegetable oils such as soybean, corn, safflower and sunflower oils. Although these fats have the positive effect of lowering the bad cholesterol (LDL), when eaten in excess, PUFAs also have the tendency to lower the good cholesterol (HDL).

In the PUFA family, there are 2 types that are classified as essential fatty acids. Essential fatty acids are vital for health and cannot be produced by the body. Every living cell in the body needs essential fatty acids to rebuild and produce new cells. There are 2 basic categories of essential fatty acids:

omega-3 fatty acids called alpha-linolenic acid
omega-6 fatty acids called linoleic acid

Too many PUFAs in the form of processed vegetable oils can create an imbalance in the ratio of omega-6 essential fatty acids to omega-3 essential fatty acids. The balance of omega-6 to omega-3 is very important and produces a teeter-totter effect. In other words, if an individual has too much of one kind, s/he will become deficient in the other. Most North Americans are chronically deficient in omega-3 essential fats. Allergies, eczema, inflammatory conditions (e.g. arthritis, colitis), constipation, attention-deficit disorder (ADD) and other learning disabilities have all been linked to a deficiency of omega-3 essential fats. While the ideal ratio of omega-6 to omega-3 fat is approximately 1:1, due to the over consumption of vegetable oils such as safflower and sunflower found in processed foods, the average ratio is more like 20:1 and 30:1. Omega-3 food sources include flaxseed oil, omega-3 eggs, deepwater fish and fish oil, walnuts and walnut oil and soy beans. Optimal sources of omega-6 are found primarily in raw nuts, seeds, legumes, borage oil, grapeseed oil and primrose oil.

Monounsaturated fats are known as the good fats. They are found in olive, canola and peanut oils and in avocadoes. These fats appear to lower bad cholesterol (LDL) and have minimal or no effect on the good cholesterol (HDL). Olive oil contains the highest amount of monounsaturated fats of all the edible oils. The best type of olive oil to buy is one labelled "extra-virgin", made from the first pressing of the olives. This oil is flavorful and can be used for cooking or in salad dressings. All oils should be stored in dark, cool places.

Trans-fatty acids are found in products such as margarine, snack foods, microwave popcorn and fried foods. Trans-fatty acids are produced when polyunsaturated oils are hydrogenated to make them into solid foods. TFAs increase the production of bad cholesterol (LDL) and decrease the production of food cholesterol (HDL). They are bad for your heart and cause hardening and narrowing of the arteries. In addition, when polyunsaturated fats are heated to high temperatures, they release free radicals which are precursors to cancer-causing agents in your body. It is best to completely eliminate trans-fatty acids in a child's diet. Check food labels carefully—if you see the words "partially hydrogenated oils", move on; this product contains trans-fatty acids.

MAXIMIZE:

- monounsaturated fats such as olive oil, avocadoes, nuts (walnuts, almonds) and seeds (sesame seeds)

- omega-3 fats such as those found in cold-water fish and fish oil

MINIMIZE:

- saturated fat such as red meat and full-fat cheeses

- trans-fatty acids such as those found in margarine and other processed food items (Look for the words "partially hydrogenated" on your label which indicate trans-fatty-acids.)

- omega-6 fats such as vegetable oils (safflower, sunflower)
  (Eaten in excess, these fats will create a dangerous inflammatory effect in the body.)

(Please refer to Appendix B for sample serving sizes of carbohydrates, proteins and fats.)

Visit www.truestarhealth.com to learn more about eating properly balanced meals. It is recommended that all our members fill out a personal nutritional profile on the Truestar website in order to receive meal plan options that fit their lifestyle, taste buds, height, weight and sex.

TRUESTAR'S 3 WEIGHT LOSS PLANS

In addition to the meals in this book being broken down into 3 macronutrients, they are also broken down according to 3 weight loss plans:

Phase 1: Metabolic Booster Plan
(rapid weight loss at 2 to 6 pounds per week)

Phase 2: Continuum Weight Loss Plan
(more gradual weight loss at 1 to 2 pounds per week)

Phase 3: Maintenance Plan

The plan you choose will vary according to your weight loss desires and health goals. For instance, if rapid weight loss is what you desire, begin by following the recipes in our Metabolic Booster Plan. As you will discover, *True Taste On The Go* is broken down into 3 sections to give you the option of all of our delicious meal plans. *(To read more about the Metabolic Booster Plan, the Continuum Weight Loss Plan or the Maintenance Plan, please refer to Appendix C.)*

PLEASE NOTE:

It is not advisable for pregnant or breast-feeding mothers to be on one of our weight loss plans (Phase 1 or Phase 2) due to higher caloric demands. One of Truestar's Maintenance Plans, the Optimal Wellness Plan, is recommended for breast-feeding or pregnant women.

HEALTHY AND DELICIOUS!

In addition to being the most important contributor to the foundation of health, food is an integral part of tradition, culture, entertaining and festivities. When we conjure up images of celebrations such as Christmas, Thanksgiving and other events, food is a large component of the enjoyment. At Truestar, our philosophy is that healthy eating and delicious food do not have to be incompatible. In fact, we have created thousands of meal plans that will tempt and please your palate and help you lose weight and feel energetic all the time. Enjoy!

Unless otherwise stated, all recipes in this book serve 1.

Phase 1:
Metabolic Booster Plan

The Metabolic Booster Plan is suitable for those who wish to lose weight in a quick, safe and easy manner. On average, in the first 4 to 6 weeks, you can expect to lose a minimum of 2 to 6 pounds or more per week. In subsequent weeks, an average weight loss of 1 to 2 pounds per week is normal.

Papaya Pineapple Orange Smoothie

approx. calories for this meal = 300

INGREDIENTS

35 g protein powder
6 fl oz water
2 fl oz orange juice
1/4 cup cubed papaya
1/4 cup crushed pineapple, in juice
1 1/2 tbsp chopped dried walnuts

INSTRUCTIONS

Combine fruit, orange juice, protein powder, water and chopped walnuts in a blender and blend thoroughly.

NUTRITIONAL VALUES

Protein %	*40.00*
Carbohydrates %	*31.00*
Fat %	*29.00*
Protein (g)	*29.00*
Carbohydrates (g)	*22.00*
Fat (g)	*9.00*
Saturated Fat (g)	*2.00*
Monounsaturated Fat (g)	*1.50*
Total Dietary Fiber (g)	*2.00*

true taste on the go

Tropical Fruit Smoothie

approx. calories for this meal = 300

INGREDIENTS

35 g protein powder

1/2 cup original soymilk

3 ice cubes

1/6 mango

1/4 small banana

2 medium strawberries

1 tsp flaxseed oil

INSTRUCTIONS

Place all ingredients in a blender. Add ice cubes (optional) and mix thoroughly.

NUTRITIONAL VALUES

Protein %	*38.00*
Carbohydrates %	*33.00*
Fat %	*29.00*
Protein (g)	*30.00*
Carbohydrates (g)	*26.00*
Fat (g)	*10.00*
Saturated Fat (g)	*2.00*
Monounsaturated Fat (g)	*1.50*
Total Dietary Fiber (g)	*3.00*

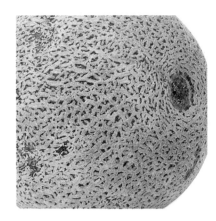

Cantaloupe Raspberry Banana Smoothie

approx. calories for this meal = 300

INGREDIENTS

40 g protein powder
10 fl oz water
3/4 cup cubed cantaloupe
1/4 medium banana
1/4 cup raspberries
1 1/2 tsp flaxseed oil

INSTRUCTIONS

Place all ingredients in a blender and blend until smooth.

NUTRITIONAL VALUES

Protein %	40.00
Carbohydrates %	31.00
Fat %	29.00
Protein (g)	30.00
Carbohydrates (g)	24.00
Fat (g)	10.00
Saturated Fat (g)	2.00
Monounsaturated Fat (g)	1.50
Total Dietary Fiber (g)	3.00

true taste on the go

Nutty Chocolate Yogurt

approx. calories for this meal = 300

INGREDIENTS

1/2 chocolate energy bar
4 oz light yogurt, any flavor
20 g protein powder
8 raw almonds

INSTRUCTIONS

Enjoy the energy bar and yogurt mixed with protein powder and almonds.

NUTRITIONAL VALUES

Protein %	*37.00*
Carbohydrates %	*35.00*
Fat %	*28.00*
Protein (g)	*28.00*
Carbohydrates (g)	*25.00*
Fat (g)	*9.00*
Saturated Fat (g)	*3.00*
Monounsaturated Fat (g)	*3.00*
Total Dietary Fiber (g)	*1.00*

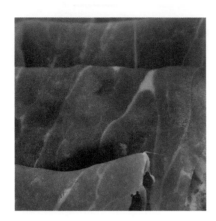

Prosciutto Melon-eh!

approx. calories for this meal = 300

INGREDIENTS

100 g prosciutto
2 honeydew melon wedges

INSTRUCTIONS

Select a ripe melon that smells sweet and gives slightly to pressure. Remove rind from two generous slices of melon and top with a little fresh pepper. Top with prosciutto slices and enjoy this classic Italian tradition.

NUTRITIONAL VALUES

Protein %	*40.00*
Carbohydrates %	*29.00*
Fat %	*31.00*
Protein (g)	*30.00*
Carbohydrates (g)	*22.00*
Fat (g)	*11.00*
Saturated Fat (g)	*4.00*
Monounsaturated Fat (g)	*0.00*
Total Dietary Fiber (g)	*2.00*

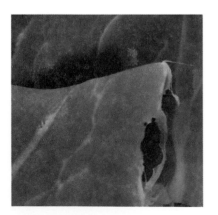

true taste on the go

Chocolate Peanut Butter Smoothie

approx. calories for this meal = 300

INGREDIENTS

30 g protein powder
1/2 cup chocolate milk (1% fat)
2 tsp creamy peanut butter
1/4 medium banana

INSTRUCTIONS

Combine chocolate milk, banana, protein powder and peanut butter in a blender until smooth.

NUTRITIONAL VALUES

Protein %	*39.00*
Carbohydrates %	*33.00*
Fat %	*28.00*
Protein (g)	*29.00*
Carbohydrates (g)	*25.00*
Fat (g)	*9.00*
Saturated Fat (g)	*3.00*
Monounsaturated Fat (g)	*0.50*
Total Dietary Fiber (g)	*2.00*

Berry Flax Yogurt
approx. calories for this meal = 300

INGREDIENTS

1/2 cup low-fat plain yogurt
20 g protein powder
1/4 cup raspberries
1/4 cup blueberries
1 tsp flaxseed oil
1 oz low-fat cheddar cheese

INSTRUCTIONS

Mix yogurt with protein powder, flaxseed oil and berries. Enjoy with cheese on the side.

NUTRITIONAL VALUES

Protein %	*39.00*
Carbohydrates %	*32.00*
Fat %	*29.00*
Protein (g)	*27.00*
Carbohydrates (g)	*22.00*
Fat (g)	*9.00*
Saturated Fat (g)	*3.00*
Monounsaturated Fat (g)	*2.00*
Total Dietary Fiber (g)	*3.00*

true taste on the go

Tasty Spicy Whites

approx. calories for this meal = 300

INGREDIENTS

5 large egg whites
1/4 tsp Tabasco hot pepper sauce
2 oz mozzarella cheese
1 slice crispbread
10 raw almonds
3/4 small apple

INSTRUCTIONS

Beat egg whites and add cheese. Fry mixture in a non-stick pan until set, adding Tabasco sauce. Fold and place on crispbread. Enjoy with fruit and almonds for dessert.

NUTRITIONAL VALUES

Protein %	40.00
Carbohydrates %	30.00
Fat %	30.00
Protein (g)	31.00
Carbohydrates (g)	23.00
Fat (g)	10.00
Saturated Fat (g)	0.50
Monounsaturated Fat (g)	5.00
Total Dietary Fiber (g)	2.00

Nacho Lunch

approx. calories for this meal = 400

INGREDIENTS

15 baked bite-size tortilla chips
1/3 cup ground soy meat
3 tbsp medium salsa picante
2 oz light cheddar cheese

INSTRUCTIONS

Place tortilla chips in a small baking dish. Layer with ground soy, salsa and shredded cheese. Place in oven or microwave and cook until cheese is melted and mixture is heated.

NUTRITIONAL VALUES

Protein %	38.00
Carbohydrates %	31.00
Fat %	31.00
Protein (g)	35.00
Carbohydrates (g)	29.00
Fat (g)	13.00
Saturated Fat (g)	2.00
Monounsaturated Fat (g)	6.00
Total Dietary Fiber (g)	1.00

true taste on the go

Honey Mustard Roast Beef Salad

approx. calories for this meal = 300

INGREDIENTS

5 oz roast beef lunch meat

2 cups mixed greens

2 tbsp non-fat honey mustard salad dressing

3 tbsp dried walnuts

1 sliced tomato

1 sliced cucumber

INSTRUCTIONS

In a bowl, combine salad (cucumber and tomato). Add roast beef slices and toss with salad dressing. Top with nuts and serve.

NUTRITIONAL VALUES

Protein %	*40.00*
Carbohydrates %	*32.00*
Fat %	*28.00*
Protein (g)	*37.00*
Carbohydrates (g)	*30.00*
Fat (g)	*12.00*
Saturated Fat (g)	*0.00*
Monounsaturated Fat (g)	*3.00*
Total Dietary Fiber (g)	*2.00*

Tossed Chicken Salad

approx. calories for this meal = 400

INGREDIENTS

4 oz grilled chicken breast
2 servings tossed side salad with balsamic vinegar
2 oz low-fat shredded cheddar cheese
1 tbsp dried sunflower seed kernels

INSTRUCTIONS

Cut chicken breast into small pieces. In a bowl, combine chicken slices, salad (4 cups lettuce, 1 cup cucumber, 4 slices tomato, 2 tbsp balsamic vinegar) and shredded cheese. Toss until thoroughly combined and sprinkle with sunflower seeds.

NUTRITIONAL VALUES

Protein %	*40.00*
Carbohydrates %	*30.00*
Fat %	*30.00*
Protein (g)	*37.00*
Carbohydrates (g)	*28.00*
Fat (g)	*12.00*
Saturated Fat (g)	*2.00*
Monounsaturated Fat (g)	*3.00*
Total Dietary Fiber (g)	*1.00*

true taste on the go

Crispy Veggie Bologna

approx. calories for this meal = 300

INGREDIENTS

5 slices veggie bologna
2 slices crispbread
1/4 avocado

INSTRUCTIONS

Top crispbread with veggie meat and avocado. Enjoy!

NUTRITIONAL VALUES

Protein %	40.00
Carbohydrates %	30.00
Fat %	30.00
Protein (g)	34.00
Carbohydrates (g)	25.00
Fat (g)	11.00
Saturated Fat (g)	2.00
Monounsaturated Fat (g)	5.00
Total Dietary Fiber (g)	8.00

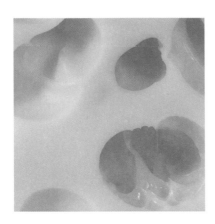

Easy Turkey Crisp

approx. calories for this meal = 400

INGREDIENTS

2 slices crispbread
4 slices roasted turkey breast
1 1/2 oz low-fat Swiss cheese
2 lettuce leaves
2 slices red tomato
1 tbsp low-fat mayonnaise

INSTRUCTIONS

Spread mayonnaise on crispbread. Place turkey, cheese, lettuce and
tomato on top and enjoy!

NUTRITIONAL VALUES

Protein %	*38.00*
Carbohydrates %	*26.00*
Fat %	*36.00*
Protein (g)	*42.00*
Carbohydrates (g)	*29.00*
Fat (g)	*18.00*
Saturated Fat (g)	*7.00*
Monounsaturated Fat (g)	*0.50*
Total Dietary Fiber (g)	*5.00*

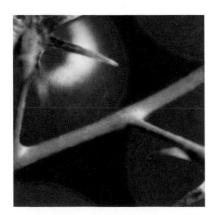

true taste on the go

Mango Strawberry
Cottage Cheese Crunch

approx. calories for this meal = 300

INGREDIENTS

3/4 cup cottage cheese (2% fat)
1/3 mango
1/3 cup strawberries
1 1/2 tbsp chopped dried walnuts

INSTRUCTIONS

Enjoy cottage cheese mixed with mango and strawberries. Sprinkle nuts on top.

NUTRITIONAL VALUES

Protein %	*37.00*
Carbohydrates %	*31.00*
Fat %	*32.00*
Protein (g)	*27.00*
Carbohydrates (g)	*22.00*
Fat (g)	*10.00*
Saturated Fat (g)	*3.00*
Monounsaturated Fat (g)	*2.00*
Total Dietary Fiber (g)	*3.00*

Turkey and Cheese Salad

approx. calories for this meal = 300

INGREDIENTS

3 cups leaf lettuce
3 slices roasted turkey breast
1 1/2 oz low-fat Swiss cheese
2 tbsp fat-free Italian salad dressing
1/2 cup chopped raw sweet red peppers
1/2 cup cucumber, with peel

INSTRUCTIONS

Toss bite-sized pieces of lettuce, peppers, cucumber (cut into pieces) and sliced turkey and cheese with the fat-free dressing.

NUTRITIONAL VALUES

Protein %	*43.00*
Carbohydrates %	*26.00*
Fat %	*31.00*
Protein (g)	*33.00*
Carbohydrates (g)	*18.00*
Fat (g)	*10.00*
Saturated Fat (g)	*5.00*
Monounsaturated Fat (g)	*0.00*
Total Dietary Fiber (g)	*3.00*

true taste on the go

Scrambled Eggs with Dill
and Smoked Salmon

approx. calories for this meal = 300

INGREDIENTS

1 large omega-3 egg
3 large egg whites
1 tbsp skim milk
1 tsp dried dill weed
1/2 medium raw spring onion or scallions
1 1/2 oz smoked salmon
3 slices crispbread

INSTRUCTIONS

In a large bowl, beat egg, egg whites, milk and dill; add salt to taste. Spray a skillet with non-fat cooking oil spray and heat over medium heat. Add sliced scallions and cook for about 8 minutes, until softened. Pour in egg mixture and cook 3 to 4 minutes, stirring occasionally, until eggs are almost set. Mix in sliced salmon, cook 1 minute more or until eggs are cooked. Enjoy with crispbread on the side.

NUTRITIONAL VALUES

Protein %	42.00
Carbohydrates %	32.00
Fat %	26.00
Protein (g)	31.00
Carbohydrates (g)	24.00
Fat (g)	8.00
Saturated Fat (g)	2.00
Monounsaturated Fat (g)	4.00
Total Dietary Fiber (g)	8.00

Green Salad with Salmon

approx. calories for this meal = 300

INGREDIENTS

6 oz canned pink salmon
1 tsp light mayonnaise
3 cups leaf lettuce
3 tbsp non-fat Italian salad dressing
3 slices crispbread

INSTRUCTIONS

Drain salmon thoroughly. Mix salmon and mayonnaise in a large bowl. Place mixed green lettuce on a plate. Scoop salmon on top of salad and top with salad dressing. Enjoy with crispbread.

NUTRITIONAL VALUES

Protein %	*37.00*
Carbohydrates %	*32.00*
Fat %	*31.00*
Protein (g)	*38.00*
Carbohydrates (g)	*32.00*
Fat (g)	*14.00*
Saturated Fat (g)	*3.00*
Monounsaturated Fat (g)	*1.00*
Total Dietary Fiber (g)	*9.00*

true taste on the go

Pesto Tuna Melt

approx. calories for this meal = 300

INGREDIENTS

2 slices crispbread
2 tsp pesto sauce with basil
2 slices red tomato
3 oz canned light tuna (in water)
1 oz non-fat mozzarella cheese

INSTRUCTIONS

Spread pesto on crispbread. Top with tomato, tuna and cheese. Put on foil and place in toaster oven. Bake for a few minutes until cheese is melted. Enjoy with a bowl of heated vegetable soup.

NUTRITIONAL VALUES

Protein %	*42.00*
Carbohydrates %	*32.00*
Fat %	*28.00*
Protein (g)	*36.00*
Carbohydrates (g)	*27.00*
Fat (g)	*10.00*
Saturated Fat (g)	*2.00*
Monounsaturated Fat (g)	*0.00*
Total Dietary Fiber (g)	*5.00*

Goldi-Lox and Cream Cheese

approx. calories for this meal = 400

INGREDIENTS

2 slices whole-grain bread
1 1/2 tbsp light cream cheese
5 oz smoked salmon
2 medium slices red tomato
1/2 cup peeled and sliced cucumber
1 tsp sliced red onion
1/2 cup strawberries

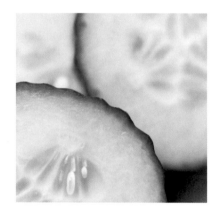

INSTRUCTIONS

Spread cream cheese on crispbread. Top with lox, cucumber, tomato and onion.
Enjoy with strawberries on the side.

NUTRITIONAL VALUES

Protein %	*36.00*
Carbohydrates %	*33.00*
Fat %	*31.00*
Protein (g)	*34.00*
Carbohydrates (g)	*31.00*
Fat (g)	*13.00*
Saturated Fat (g)	*5.00*
Monounsaturated Fat (g)	*4.00*
Total Dietary Fiber (g)	*9.00*

true taste on the go

Healthy Hamburger

approx. calories for this meal = 400

TRUE FACTS

When purchasing grains, ensure that they are either 100% whole-wheat or made from whole grains.

INGREDIENTS

1 veggie burger
1 cup tossed side salad with olive oil and balsamic vinegar
1 oz low-fat cheddar cheese
1/2 whole-grain hamburger bun

INSTRUCTIONS

Prepare veggie burgers following package instructions. Place veggie burger onto 1/2 toasted whole-grain bun. Melt low-fat cheese over top in microwave. Add 1 tsp of mustard, ketchup or relish, if desired. Enjoy with side salad.

NUTRITIONAL VALUES

Protein %	*42.00*
Carbohydrates %	*28.00*
Fat %	*30.00*
Protein (g)	*41.00*
Carbohydrates (g)	*28.00*
Fat (g)	*13.00*
Saturated Fat (g)	*2.00*
Monounsaturated Fat (g)	*2.00*
Total Dietary Fiber (g)	*1.00*

Turkey Chili

approx. calories for this meal = 400

INGREDIENTS

1/2 tsp extra-virgin olive oil
5 oz lean ground turkey
1/4 cup chopped onion
1/4 cup canned red kidney beans
1 tsp chili powder
1/2 tsp garlic powder
1 tsp ground black pepper
1 cup canned stewed tomatoes

INSTRUCTIONS

Heat oil in a large non-stick pan over medium-high heat. Add ground turkey and sauté for 5 minutes or until lightly browned. Stir often. Add onions, kidney beans, chili powder, garlic powder, pepper and stewed tomatoes. Simmer for approximately 20 minutes. Place in a bowl and serve.

NUTRITIONAL VALUES

Protein %	*38.00*
Carbohydrates %	*32.00*
Fat %	*30.00*
Protein (g)	*35.00*
Carbohydrates (g)	*30.00*
Fat (g)	*13.00*
Saturated Fat (g)	*3.00*
Monounsaturated Fat (g)	*0.00*
Total Dietary Fiber (g)	*9.00*

true taste on the go

Speedy Tuna Salad

approx. calories for this meal = 400

INGREDIENTS

5 oz canned albacore tuna (in water)

2 tbsp diced celery

2 tsp light mayonnaise

1/2 cup sliced raw sweet red pepper

1 1/2 tsp extra-virgin olive oil

1/2 small pear

1/2 tbsp chopped onion

2 tbsp chopped carrots

3 cups romaine lettuce

1/2 cup peeled and sliced cucumber

1 tbsp balsamic vinegar

INSTRUCTIONS

Combine lettuce and vegetables in a bowl and add dressing (olive oil and balsamic vinegar). In another bowl, add tuna, onions, celery, carrots and mayonnaise. Mix until it is completely combined. Arrange salad in plate and top with a scoop of tuna salad and serve. Enjoy with fruit for dessert.

NUTRITIONAL VALUES

Protein %	*40.00*
Carbohydrates %	*30.00*
Fat %	*30.00*
Protein (g)	*40.00*
Carbohydrates (g)	*29.00*
Fat (g)	*13.00*
Saturated Fat (g)	*2.00*
Monounsaturated Fat (g)	*1.00*
Total Dietary Fiber (g)	*4.00*

Turkey Spinach Salad

approx. calories for this meal = 400

INGREDIENTS

4 oz roasted turkey breast

4 cups raw spinach

1/2 cup mandarin orange sections

2 tbsp sliced raw almonds, toasted

2 tbsp non-fat honey mustard salad dressing

INSTRUCTIONS

Slice cooked turkey. In a bowl, combine spinach, mandarin orange sections, toasted almonds and salad dressing. Toss and top with turkey.

NUTRITIONAL VALUES

Protein %	*40.00*
Carbohydrates %	*28.00*
Fat %	*32.00*
Protein (g)	*40.00*
Carbohydrates (g)	*27.00*
Fat (g)	*14.00*
Saturated Fat (g)	*3.00*
Monounsaturated Fat (g)	*6.00*
Total Dietary Fiber (g)	*8.00*

true taste on the go

Warm Curried Tuna Sandwich

approx. calories for this meal = 400

INGREDIENTS

1 1/2 tsp vegetable oil
4 oz canned light tuna (in water)
1/4 cup sliced raw onion
1 garlic clove
1/2 tsp curry powder
1/2 green chili pepper
1 1/2 tbsp coriander
2 slices whole-grain bread, toasted
2 medium slices red tomato

INSTRUCTIONS

In a non-stick pan, add oil and place over medium-high heat. Add sliced onion and chopped garlic. Stir-fry until onion turns brown. Add curry powder and tuna. Mix well. Turn heat to low and add chopped green chili and chopped coriander. Mix. Add salt and pepper to taste. Serve on toasted bread with sliced tomato.

NUTRITIONAL VALUES

Protein %	38.00
Carbohydrates %	30.00
Fat %	32.00
Protein (g)	28.00
Carbohydrates (g)	22.00
Fat (g)	11.00
Saturated Fat (g)	1.00
Monounsaturated Fat (g)	4.00
Total Dietary Fiber (g)	7.00

Quick Corn and Tuna Salad
approx. calories for this meal = 400

INGREDIENTS

1/3 cup canned corn niblets
1 red tomato
5 oz canned albacore tuna (in water)
2 tsp extra-virgin olive oil
2 slices crispbread

INSTRUCTIONS

Mix corn niblets, tuna and chopped tomatoes in a bowl. Add olive oil and salt to taste and mix well. Enjoy with crispbread.

NUTRITIONAL VALUES

Protein %	36.00
Carbohydrates %	32.00
Fat %	32.00
Protein (g)	38.00
Carbohydrates (g)	35.00
Fat (g)	16.00
Saturated Fat (g)	4.00
Monounsaturated Fat (g)	2.00
Total Dietary Fiber (g)	3.00

true taste on the go

German Turkey Salad

approx. calories for this meal = 400

INGREDIENTS

1/2 tsp extra-virgin olive oil

2 cups shredded cabbage

1 cup cauliflower

1/2 tsp balsamic vinegar

2 tsp minced garlic

2 fl oz water

1/3 tsp chili powder

4 oz lean ground turkey

1 cup broccoli florets

3/4 cup sliced raw sweet red pepper

1/2 tsp Worcestershire sauce

1 tbsp tomato purée

1/4 tsp dried tarragon

INSTRUCTIONS

Combine oil, ground turkey, broccoli, cauliflower, pepper strips, balsamic vinegar, Worcestershire sauce, minced garlic, tomato paste and other spices in a non-stick pan. Cook until turkey is browned and vegetables are tender. Cover and simmer for 5 minutes until mixture is hot, stirring occasionally to blend flavors. Arrange shredded cabbage on a large plate. Spoon ground turkey and vegetables on top of cabbage. Sprinkle with salt and pepper.

NUTRITIONAL VALUES

Protein %	*38.00*
Carbohydrates %	*32.00*
Fat %	*30.00*
Protein (g)	*31.00*
Carbohydrates (g)	*26.00*
Fat (g)	*11.00*
Saturated Fat (g)	*3.00*
Monounsaturated Fat (g)	*0.00*
Total Dietary Fiber (g)	*9.00*

Phase 2: Continuum Weight Loss Plan

The Continuum Weight Loss Plan is designed for individuals who have successfully completed the Metabolic Booster Plan and wish to include more whole grains and carbohydrates into their diet, or for those who desire a more gradual weight loss approach. Once you have successfully completed Phase 1, your metabolism should be working at a faster pace and you should not gain any weight when switching to Phase 2. If you do find yourself gaining weight, simply switch back to the Metabolic Booster Plan for another 4 to 6 weeks. In Phase 2, you can expect to lose weight at approximately 1 to 2 pounds per week.

Sweet Yogurt Supreme

approx. calories for this meal = 300

INGREDIENTS

6 oz plain light yogurt
15 g protein powder
1/4 cup blueberries
1 tsp honey
2 tbsp chopped almonds

INSTRUCTIONS

Place yogurt, protein powder, blueberries and honey in a bowl. Mix well.
Sprinkle with almonds and serve.

NUTRITIONAL VALUES

Protein %	27.00
Carbohydrates %	43.00
Fat %	30.00
Protein (g)	24.00
Carbohydrates (g)	37.00
Fat (g)	12.00
Saturated Fat (g)	1.00
Monounsaturated Fat (g)	6.00
Total Dietary Fiber (g)	2.00

true taste on the go

Orange Date Almond Oatmeal

approx. calories for this meal = 300

INGREDIENTS

1/2 cup slow-cooking oatmeal
2 fl oz 100% orange juice
4 fl oz filtered water
1 dry date, chopped
1/8 tsp ground nutmeg
25 g protein powder
2 tbsp chopped almonds

INSTRUCTIONS

In a pan, bring juice, water and nutmeg to a boil. Stir in slow-cooking oatmeal and chopped date. Return to a boil, reduce heat and cook for about 5 minutes. Mix in protein powder. Top with chopped almonds.

NUTRITIONAL VALUES

Protein %	*27.00*
Carbohydrates %	*44.00*
Fat %	*29.00*
Protein (g)	*21.00*
Carbohydrates (g)	*34.00*
Fat (g)	*10.00*
Saturated Fat (g)	*2.00*
Monounsaturated Fat (g)	*6.00*
Total Dietary Fiber (g)	*2.00*

Chocolate Monkey Smoothie

approx. calories for this meal = 300

INGREDIENTS

8 fl oz soymilk
3 tbsp unsweetened cocoa powder
10 g protein powder
1/2 small banana
1 tsp flaxseed oil

INSTRUCTIONS

Add all ingredients in a blender and mix until smooth.

NUTRITIONAL VALUES

Protein %	*24.00*
Carbohydrates %	*48.00*
Fat %	*28.00*
Protein (g)	*18.00*
Carbohydrates (g)	*37.00*
Fat (g)	*10.00*
Saturated Fat (g)	*2.00*
Monounsaturated Fat (g)	*1.00*
Total Dietary Fiber (g)	*4.00*

true taste on the go

Apple Cinnamon Power Oatmeal

approx. calories for this meal = 300

INGREDIENTS

1/2 cup oatmeal cereal

3/4 cup water

1/4 cup 100% apple juice

1 tbsp dried apple

1/4 tsp ground cinnamon

25 g protein powder

2 tbsp chopped almonds

INSTRUCTIONS

In a pan, combine oats, water, apple juice, chopped dried apples and cinnamon. Bring to a boil. Cover and reduce heat to low. Simmer for 5 minutes. Remove from heat and add protein powder. Cover. Let stand for a few minutes. Top with chopped nuts.

NUTRITIONAL VALUES

Protein %	*28.00*
Carbohydrates %	*42.00*
Fat %	*30.00*
Protein (g)	*21.00*
Carbohydrates (g)	*33.00*
Fat (g)	*10.00*
Saturated Fat (g)	*2.00*
Monounsaturated Fat (g)	*6.00*
Total Dietary Fiber (g)	*1.00*

Delicious Apple Protein Smoothie

approx. calories for this meal = 300

INGREDIENTS

20 g protein powder
1/2 cup plain yogurt
4 fl oz 100% apple juice
1/4 small banana
1 tsp flaxseed oil

INSTRUCTIONS

Place all ingredients in a blender. Blend on high setting until smooth.

NUTRITIONAL VALUES

Protein %	28.00
Carbohydrates %	42.00
Fat %	30.00
Protein (g)	21.00
Carbohydrates (g)	31.00
Fat (g)	10.00
Saturated Fat (g)	4.00
Monounsaturated Fat (g)	1.00
Total Dietary Fiber (g)	1.00

true taste on the go

Date Almond and Banana Smoothie

approx. calories for this meal = 400

INGREDIENTS

15 g soy protein powder

8 fl oz low-fat vanilla soymilk

2 dry dates

1/4 small banana

2 tsp almond butter

INSTRUCTIONS

Soak dates in hot water for 5 minutes. Place soymilk, dates and banana in a blender. Blend ingredients at a low speed as you add the almond butter. Increase to a higher setting and blend for approximately 2 minutes.

NUTRITIONAL VALUES

Protein %	26.00
Carbohydrates %	49.00
Fat %	25.00
Protein (g)	20.00
Carbohydrates (g)	39.00
Fat (g)	8.00
Saturated Fat (g)	1.00
Monounsaturated Fat (g)	5.00
Total Dietary Fiber (g)	5.00

Fruity Cookies 'N Cream Waffle Breakfast

approx. calories for this meal = 400

INGREDIENTS

8 oz plain yogurt
15 g protein powder
1/4 cup strawberry halves
2 tsp jam or preserves (your choice)
1 chocolate wafer cookie
1 whole-grain waffle
1 tsp maple syrup

INSTRUCTIONS

Mix yogurt and protein powder in a large bowl. Add jam, strawberries and crushed cookies. Stir well. Serve with a waffle prepared by following package instructions. Top waffle with maple syrup.

NUTRITIONAL VALUES

Protein %	26.00
Carbohydrates %	38.00
Fat %	36.00
Protein (g)	26.00
Carbohydrates (g)	42.00
Fat (g)	14.00
Saturated Fat (g)	6.00
Monounsaturated Fat (g)	5.00
Total Dietary Fiber (g)	3.00

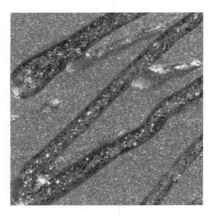

true taste on the go

Mexican Pocket

approx. calories for this meal = 200

INGREDIENTS

1 medium whole-wheat tortilla wrap
3/4 oz non-fat cheddar cheese
1/2 oz reduced-fat Monterey Jack cheese
1 tbsp chopped or sliced red tomato
1 tbsp chopped raw sweet red pepper
1 tbsp canned black beans
2 tsp chopped onion
1 tsp medium salsa

INSTRUCTIONS

Preheat oven to 400 °F. Spray a baking dish with cooking oil spray. Place all ingredients onto half of the tortilla and fold tortilla over and close with toothpicks to seal in the ingredients. Bake in oven until tortilla is lightly browned and cheese is melted. Use hot salsa, as desired.

NUTRITIONAL VALUES

Protein %	*28.00*
Carbohydrates %	*43.00*
Fat %	*29.00*
Protein (g)	*16.00*
Carbohydrates (g)	*23.00*
Fat (g)	*6.00*
Saturated Fat (g)	*3.00*
Monounsaturated Fat (g)	*1.00*
Total Dietary Fiber (g)	*3.00*

Spring Veggie Wrap
approx. calories for this meal = 400

INGREDIENTS

1 serving low-fat flour tortilla

2 tbsp grated carrots

2 1/2 oz non-fat cheddar
  cheese

1 romain lettuce leaf

2 tsp extra-virgin olive oil

1 dash table salt

2 tbsp hummus

3 tbsp peeled and chopped cucumber

3 cups shredded or chopped
  iceberg lettuce

1 cup sliced raw green pepper

2 tbsp balsamic vinegar

1/8 tsp ground black pepper

INSTRUCTIONS

Spread hummus on a tortilla. Layer lettuce, shredded carrots, cucumber and cheese in the center of the tortilla. Roll up. Serve with a side salad dressed with oil, vinegar and salt and pepper, as desired.

NUTRITIONAL VALUES

Protein %	*30.00*
Carbohydrates %	*40.00*
Fat %	*30.00*
Protein (g)	*27.00*
Carbohydrates (g)	*36.00*
Fat (g)	*11.00*
Saturated Fat (g)	*1.00*
Monounsaturated Fat (g)	*2.00*
Total Dietary Fiber (g)	*16.00*

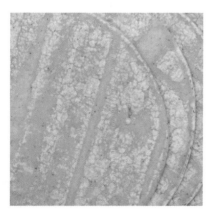

true taste on the go

Bok Choy Chicken Salad

approx. calories for this meal = 400

INGREDIENTS

2 oz roasted boneless skinless chicken breast

1 tbsp red wine vinegar

2 tsp extra-virgin olive oil

1 tsp sugar

1/2 tsp light soy sauce

2 tsp slivered raw almonds

1 tsp sesame seed

4 cups bok choy, shredded

1/2 cup grated carrots

1/4 cup chopped raw spring onion

1 cup mandarin orange sections

INSTRUCTIONS

In a bowl, mix dressing: vinegar, olive oil, sugar and soy sauce. In another bowl, combine chopped bok choy, onions, carrots, almonds, diced chicken and dressing. Serve with fruit for dessert.

NUTRITIONAL VALUES

Protein %	28.00
Carbohydrates %	42.00
Fat %	30.00
Protein (g)	30.00
Carbohydrates (g)	44.00
Fat (g)	14.00
Saturated Fat (g)	3.00
Monounsaturated Fat (g)	3.00
Total Dietary Fiber (g)	8.00

Warm Turkey Salad

approx. calories for this meal = 400

INGREDIENTS

1 tsp extra-virgin olive oil
1 1/2 cup broccoli florets
3/4 cup sliced raw sweet red pepper
1/2 tsp balsamic vinegar
2 tsp minced garlic
2 fl oz filtered water
1/4 tsp ground oregano
1/4 tsp dried basil
1/2 tsp paprika
3 cups shredded cabbage

4 oz raw ground turkey
1 1/2 cup cauliflower
3/4 cup sliced raw green pepper
1/2 tsp Worcestershire sauce
1 tbsp tomato purée
1/4 tsp dried tarragon
1/4 tsp dried parsley
1/8 tsp chili powder
1/4 tsp dried dill weed

INSTRUCTIONS

Combine oil, ground turkey, broccoli, cauliflower, pepper strips, balsamic vinegar, Worcestershire sauce, minced garlic, tomato paste, water and other spices in a non-stick pan. Cook until turkey is browned and vegetables are tender. Cover and simmer for 5 minutes until mixture is hot, stirring occasionally to blend flavors. Arrange shredded cabbage on a large plate. Spoon ground turkey and vegetables onto cabbage. Sprinkle with salt and pepper and serve.

NUTRITIONAL VALUES

Protein %	30.00		
Carbohydrates %	38.00		
Fat %	32.00		
Protein (g)	31.00	*Saturated Fat (g)*	3.00
Carbohydrates (g)	40.00	*Monounsaturated Fat (g)*	3.00
Fat (g)	14.00	*Total Dietary Fiber (g)*	15.00

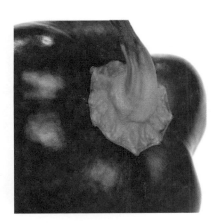

true taste on the go

Ham and Swiss Crisp

approx. calories for this meal = 400

INGREDIENTS

3 slices crispbread
3 oz extra-lean sliced ham
1 oz non-fat Swiss cheese
1 lettuce leaf
1 tbsp mustard
1 tsp mayonnaise
1 medium apple

INSTRUCTIONS

Spread mustard and mayonnaise on crispbread. Top with ham, cheese and lettuce. Enjoy with fruit.

NUTRITIONAL VALUES

Protein %	29.00
Carbohydrates %	42.00
Fat %	29.00
Protein (g)	25.00
Carbohydrates (g)	38.00
Fat (g)	11.00
Saturated Fat (g)	2.00
Monounsaturated Fat (g)	2.00
Total Dietary Fiber (g)	10.00

Deli Chicken Crisp Sandwich
approx. calories for this meal = 400

INGREDIENTS

3 slices crispbread
3 oz chicken breast lunch meat
1 oz low-fat Swiss cheese
1 tbsp mustard
1 serving tossed side salad
2 tbsp fat-free Italian salad dressing
1 small apple

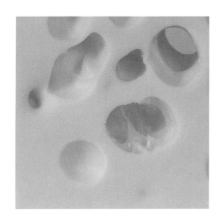

INSTRUCTIONS

Spread mustard onto crispbread and top with cheese and sliced deli chicken. Enjoy with a side salad (2 cups lettuce, 1/2 cup sliced cucumber, 2 tomato slices, dressing), and an apple for dessert.

NUTRITIONAL VALUES

Protein %	*30.00*
Carbohydrates %	*43.00*
Fat %	*27.00*
Protein (g)	*29.00*
Carbohydrates (g)	*41.00*
Fat (g)	*11.00*
Saturated Fat (g)	*3.00*
Monounsaturated Fat (g)	*0.00*
Total Dietary Fiber (g)	*10.00*

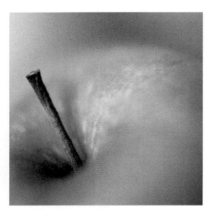

true taste on the go

Zesty Indian Spinach Chicken Salad

approx. calories for this meal = 400

INGREDIENTS

2 1/2 oz roasted boneless skinless chicken breast

1/4 tsp curry powder

1/6 tsp ground cumin

1/2 cup quartered or chopped apple

1 tbsp raisins

1 slice high-fiber snack bread

1 1/2 tsp extra-virgin olive oil

1 tbsp white vinegar

1/6 tsp mustard powder

4 cups raw spinach

2 tsp raw peanuts

1 tbsp chopped raw spring onion

1/2 mango

INSTRUCTIONS

In a small bowl, whisk together salad dressing: oil, vinegar, curry powder, salt, mustard and cumin. Cut chicken into cubes and combine with spinach, cubed apples, peanuts, raisins and onions. Serve with crispbread and enjoy with fruit for dessert.

NUTRITIONAL VALUES

Protein %	*28.00*
Carbohydrates %	*42.00*
Fat %	*30.00*
Protein (g)	*30.00*
Carbohydrates (g)	*44.00*
Fat (g)	*13.00*
Saturated Fat (g)	*3.00*
Monounsaturated Fat (g)	*3.00*
Total Dietary Fiber (g)	*10.00*

Rosy Red Snapper with Mashed Sweet Potato and Green Beans

approx. calories for this meal = 400

INGREDIENTS

4 oz raw snapper
2 tsp extra-virgin olive oil
1/4 cup lemon juice
3/4 cup canned mashed sweet potato
1/2 cup green beans

INSTRUCTIONS

Heat oil in a non-stick frying pan over medium-high heat. Season red snapper with lemon juice and your choice of seasonings. Place red snapper in the pan and sauté for approximately 4 minutes per side or until the fish flakes easily. Place cooked fish on a plate and add lemon juice to taste. Serve with mashed potato and steamed vegetables.

NUTRITIONAL VALUES

Protein %	*26.00*
Carbohydrates %	*48.00*
Fat %	*26.00*
Protein (g)	*29.00*
Carbohydrates (g)	*49.00*
Fat (g)	*11.00*
Saturated Fat (g)	*1.00*
Monounsaturated Fat (g)	*0.00*
Total Dietary Fiber (g)	*5.00*

true taste on the go

Scallops and Vegetables with Kamut Pasta

approx. calories for this meal = 400

INGREDIENTS

1 1/2 oz dry kamut penne pasta
1/2 tsp minced garlic
1/6 tsp salt
1/6 tsp ground red chili pepper
1/4 cup chopped or sliced red tomato
1 1/2 tsp grated parmesan cheese

2 tsp extra-virgin olive oil
1/2 small raw zucchini
2 tbsp chopped raw sweet red pepper
1 tbsp fresh basil
5 oz raw scallops

INSTRUCTIONS

Prepare pasta according to package directions. In a large non-stick pan, heat oil and add garlic; sauté until tender. Add diced zucchini, peppers, salt and chili pepper. Sauté for approximately 10 minutes. Add chopped tomatoes, scallops and basil. Simmer for about 5 minutes or until scallops are opaque. Pour sauce over cooked pasta and sprinkle with parmesan cheese.

NUTRITIONAL VALUES

Protein %	32.00
Carbohydrates %	39.00
Fat %	29.00
Protein (g)	33.00
Carbohydrates (g)	40.00
Fat (g)	13.00
Saturated Fat (g)	2.00
Monounsaturated Fat (g)	0.00
Total Dietary Fiber (g)	6.00

Snappy Snapper
approx. calories for this meal = 400

INGREDIENTS

4 oz raw snapper
1/2 tsp extra-virgin olive oil
1/2 cup cooked brown basmati rice
7 boiled asparagus spears
1 side salad

INSTRUCTIONS

Preheat oven or grill. Season fish with desired spices, drizzle with olive oil and place on grill or in a pan in the oven. Cook for 10 minutes or until fish flakes easily with a fork. Serve with rice and vegetables and a side salad (2 cups lettuce, 1/2 cup cucumber, 2 slices tomato, 1 tbsp balsamic vinegar, 1 tsp olive oil).

NUTRITIONAL VALUES

Protein %	31.00
Carbohydrates %	39.00
Fat %	30.00
Protein (g)	30.00
Carbohydrates (g)	37.00
Fat (g)	13.00
Saturated Fat (g)	1.00
Monounsaturated Fat (g)	0.00
Total Dietary Fiber (g)	2.00

true taste on the go

Tuna Nicoise Salad

approx. calories for this meal = 400

INGREDIENTS

1 boiled potato

3 1/2 oz canned tuna (in water)

1/4 cup peeled and sliced cucumber

1/2 large hard-boiled egg

1/2 tsp chopped parsley

2 tsp olive oil

1/8 tsp mustard

3 cups romaine lettuce

1/4 cup green beans

1/2 red tomato

1/8 tsp minced garlic

2 tsp red wine vinegar

1 1/2 tsp lemon juice

1/2 tsp chopped scallions
  or spring onions

INSTRUCTIONS

Cook potato, uncovered, in salted water until tender when pierced with a fork. Drain, peel and slice. Combine with chopped green onion and dash of salt and pepper; set aside. Snip the ends off the green beans. Cook green beans in salted water covered, until crisp, yet tender; drain. Arrange lettuce, green beans, tuna, potato slices, cucumber slices, tomato wedges and egg slices on a plate. For dressing, mix garlic, parsley, onion, vinegar, lemon juice, mustard and oil in a small bowl. Drizzle dressing over salad. Serve chilled.

NUTRITIONAL VALUES

Protein %	*31.00*
Carbohydrates %	*42.00*
Fat %	*27.00*
Protein (g)	*31.00*
Carbohydrates (g)	*41.00*
Fat (g)	*12.00*
Saturated Fat (g)	*1.00*
Monounsaturated Fat (g)	*1.00*
Total Dietary Fiber (g)	*4.00*

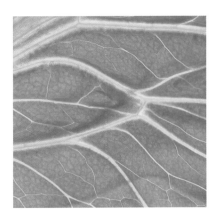

Chicken Salad Supreme

approx. calories for this meal = 400

INGREDIENTS

2 1/2 oz roasted skinless
  chicken breast

1 raw spring onion

1/2 cup raw snow peas

3 cups romaine lettuce

1 1/2 tbsp slivered raw almonds

1 tsp white vinegar

1 tsp light teriyaki sauce

1/2 cup chopped raw sweet
  red pepper

1/2 cup chopped carrots

1/2 cup peeled and chopped cucumber

2 tsp dried cilantro

1 tsp sugar

1 1/2 tsp sesame oil

INSTRUCTIONS

In a bowl, combine chicken, chopped onions, carrot, peppers, snow peas, cucumber, lettuce, cilantro and almonds. In another bowl, combine dressing ingredients: sugar, vinegar, sesame oil and teriyaki sauce. Pour dressing over salad and serve.

NUTRITIONAL VALUES

Protein %	28.00
Carbohydrates %	42.00
Fat %	30.00
Protein (g)	29.00
Carbohydrates (g)	42.00
Fat (g)	14.00
Saturated Fat (g)	2.00
Monounsaturated Fat (g)	4.00
Total Dietary Fiber (g)	7.00

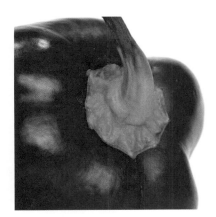

true taste on the go

Barbecue Asian Turkey Breast

approx. calories for this meal = 400

INGREDIENTS

3 1/2 oz raw boneless, skinless
  turkey breast
2 tsp soy sauce
1/4 tsp minced garlic
1 ear boiled sweet corn on the cob
1 cup broccoli florets

3 tbsp barbecue sauce
1 tbsp scallions or spring onions
1 1/2 tsp whole-dried sesame seeds
1/8 tsp ground ginger
2 tsp butter

INSTRUCTIONS

Combine barbecue sauce, chopped onions, soy sauce, sesame seeds, garlic and ginger in a measuring cup. Remove 1/3 of the mixture, cover and refrigerate. Pierce turkey breast using a fork. Combine turkey and remaining 2/3 of marinade in a self-closing plastic bag. Seal bag and refrigerate overnight. Prepare grill. Cook turkey breast for 25 to 30 minutes or until thoroughly cooked. During the last few minutes of cooking, brush turkey with reserved marinade. Serve with steamed broccoli and boiled corn on the cob with butter.

NUTRITIONAL VALUES

Protein %	32.00
Carbohydrates %	39.00
Fat %	29.00
Protein (g)	33.00
Carbohydrates (g)	39.00
Fat (g)	13.00
Saturated Fat (g)	1.00
Monounsaturated Fat (g)	2.00
Total Dietary Fiber (g)	1.00

Teriyaki Sesame Chicken

approx. calories for this meal = 400

INGREDIENTS

4 oz raw boneless skinless chicken breast
1/4 cup teriyaki sauce
1 tbsp lemon juice
1/2 tsp minced garlic
1/2 tsp sesame oil
1/2 tbsp roasted and toasted whole sesame seeds
1 serving tossed side salad
1 small baked sweet potato

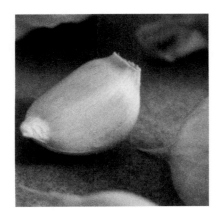

INSTRUCTIONS

Place chicken, teriyaki sauce, lemon juice, garlic and sesame oil in a resealable plastic bag. Seal and shake. Marinate in refrigerator overnight. Preheat grill on medium-high heat and lightly oil. Grill marinated chicken for about 5 minutes per side or until meat is no longer pink inside. Sprinkle sesame seeds on top of chicken. Serve with a baked sweet potato and side salad (2 cups lettuce, 1/2 cup sliced cucumbers, 2 tomato slices, 1 tbsp balsamic vinegar, 1 tsp olive oil).

NUTRITIONAL VALUES

Protein %	*31.00*
Carbohydrates %	*39.00*
Fat %	*30.00*
Protein (g)	*28.00*
Carbohydrates (g)	*36.00*
Fat (g)	*13.00*
Saturated Fat (g)	*2.00*
Monounsaturated Fat (g)	*1.00*
Total Dietary Fiber (g)	*3.00*

true taste on the go

Tempeh Pepper Wrap

approx. calories for this meal = 400

INGREDIENTS

1/2 tsp olive oil

1 1/2 tsp soy sauce

1/4 cup chopped raw green pepper

3/4 tsp dehydrated onion flakes

1 1/2 oz non-fat cheddar cheese

1/4 cup chopped raw sweet red pepper

2 oz tempeh

3/4 tsp lime juice

1/4 cup sliced mushroom

1 medium whole-wheat tortilla wrap

3/4 tsp chopped red and
    green hot chili peppers

INSTRUCTIONS

Heat oil in a non-stick skillet over medium heat. Sauté bite-sized pieces of tempeh with soy sauce and lime juice until tempeh browns. Mix in red and green peppers, mushrooms, chili peppers and onion. Increase heat to medium-high and cook until liquids have reduced, stirring occasionally. Place mixture into tortilla and top with grated cheese. Enjoy with a glass of soymilk.

NUTRITIONAL VALUES

Protein %	*30.00*
Carbohydrates %	*44.00*
Fat %	*26.00*
Protein (g)	*29.00*
Carbohydrates (g)	*44.00*
Fat (g)	*12.00*
Saturated Fat (g)	*2.00*
Monounsaturated Fat (g)	*3.00*
Total Dietary Fiber (g)	*4.00*

Beany Tofu Tacos
approx. calories for this meal = 400

INGREDIENTS

4 oz light extra-firm tofu
1/2 cup dark red kidney beans
1 tsp taco seasoning mix
2 taco shells
2 tbsp shredded light-mild cheddar cheese
1/4 cup shredded iceberg lettuce
1/4 cup mild home-style salsa
1 1/2 tbsp light sour cream

INSTRUCTIONS

Crumble tofu in a non-stick pan and add taco seasoning to taste. Add beans. Stir-fry until mixture is heated thoroughly and seasoning is mixed throughout. Spoon into taco shells and top with shredded cheese, shredded lettuce, sour cream and salsa.

NUTRITIONAL VALUES

Protein %	*26.00*
Carbohydrates %	*47.00*
Fat %	*27.00*
Protein (g)	*26.00*
Carbohydrates (g)	*49.00*
Fat (g)	*12.00*
Saturated Fat (g)	*5.00*
Monounsaturated Fat (g)	*0.00*
Total Dietary Fiber (g)	*10.00*

true taste on the go

Beef Fajitas

approx. calories for this meal = 400

INGREDIENTS

1 medium whole-wheat tortilla wrap

1/2 tbsp lemon juice

1 tsp parsley

1 dash table salt

1 serving cooking oil spray

1/2 cup sliced raw green pepper

1/4 cup medium salsa

1 cup peeled and sliced cucumber

1 tsp extra-virgin olive oil

4 oz lean eye of beef round

1/8 tsp chili powder

1/8 tsp minced garlic

1 dash ground black pepper

1/4 medium raw onion

1/2 red tomato

2 cups romaine lettuce

2 slices red tomato

1 tbsp balsamic vinegar

INSTRUCTIONS

Cut steak into thin strips. Place in a bowl with lemon juice, chili powder, parsley, garlic, salt and pepper and set aside. Coat a non-stick pan with cooking oil spray and heat over medium-high heat. Add marinated beef strips and stir-fry until beef is browned. Add peppers and onions. Stir-fry for 3 minutes or until the vegetables and beef are cooked to the desired tenderness. Add the tomato and salsa. Spoon beef and vegetable mixture into tortillas and roll up. Serve with a side salad (lettuce, cucumber, tomato, oil and vinegar).

NUTRITIONAL VALUES

Protein %	30.00		
Carbohydrates %	42.00		
Fat %	28.00		
Protein (g)	29.00	*Saturated Fat (g)*	1.00
Carbohydrates (g)	40.00	*Monounsaturated Fat (g)*	5.00
Fat (g)	12.00	*Total Dietary Fiber (g)*	5.00

Fiesta Black Bean and Chicken Salad

approx. calories for this meal = 400

INGREDIENTS

1/2 cup canned black beans

3 cups leaf lettuce

1/2 cup chopped raw sweet red pepper

1/4 cup chopped onion

2 1/2 tsp olive oil

1 dash table salt

4 oz grilled chicken breast

1/2 cup diced celery

1/2 cup chopped or sliced red tomato

2 tbsp lime juice

2 tsp chopped parsley

1 dash ground black pepper

INSTRUCTIONS

In a large bowl, combine black beans, grilled and diced chicken, celery, red pepper, onion and tomato. Pour dressing over mixture and toss to coat. Marinate salad for 10 minutes before serving. Dressing: lime juice, oil, parsley, salt and pepper.

NUTRITIONAL VALUES

Protein %	*30.00*
Carbohydrates %	*40.00*
Fat %	*30.00*
Protein (g)	*33.00*
Carbohydrates (g)	*42.00*
Fat (g)	*15.00*
Saturated Fat (g)	*0.00*
Monounsaturated Fat (g)	*0.00*
Total Dietary Fiber (g)	*10.00*

true taste on the go

Fun Bow-Tie Pasta Surprise

approx. calories for this meal = 400

TRUE FACTS

Monounsaturated fats (good fats) have been shown to lower bad cholesterol, called low-density lipoprotein (LDL) and raise good cholesterol, known as high-density lipoprotein (HDL). Monounsaturated fats are found in olives, olive oil, canola oil, peanut oil, cashews, almonds and most other nuts and avocadoes.

INGREDIENTS

1 serving olive oil cooking spray
1/4 cup chopped onion
1/2 cup boiled spinach
1/4 cup canned white beans
1/2 oz slivered, blanched almonds

1 1/2 oz whole-wheat bow tie pasta
1 clove garlic
3 tbsp canned vegetable broth
1/4 cup shredded parmesan cheese

INSTRUCTIONS

Cook pasta following package instructions. Drain and keep warm. Meanwhile, spray a large pan with olive oil cooking spray. Sauté onions and garlic for approximately 5 minutes. Add spinach and broth. Bring liquid to a boil. Reduce heat and simmer, covering until spinach is wilted, approximately 5 to 10 minutes. Add beans and stir for approximately 3 minutes or until broth is evaporated. Stir mixture into pasta. Add nuts and half the parmesan cheese. Toss. Sprinkle with remaining cheese.

NUTRITIONAL VALUES

Protein %	26.00
Carbohydrates %	46.00
Fat %	28.00
Protein (g)	26.00
Carbohydrates (g)	47.00
Fat (g)	13.00
Saturated Fat (g)	5.00
Monounsaturated Fat (g)	5.00
Total Dietary Fiber (g)	12.00

Garden Green Soy Bean Salad

approx. calories for this meal = 400

INGREDIENTS

3/4 tsp olive oil

6 oz light extra-firm tofu

1/4 cup chopped carrots

1/4 cup diced cantaloupe

1 tsp roasted and toasted whole
  sesame seeds

1/2 tsp lemon peel

2/3 tbsp apple cider vinegar

1/3 cup lemon juice

1/2 cup raw green soy beans

1/3 raw parsnip

1/3 cup raw oriental radish (daikon)

1/4 cup diced celery

1/2 canned red chili pepper,
  without seeds

1/3 tbsp brown sugar

1/3 tbsp soy sauce

INSTRUCTIONS

Bring a pot of salted water to a boil. Boil soy beans until just tender, about
5 minutes. Drain beans, reserving water and transfer to a bowl. In the same
water, cook diced parsnips, carrots and daikon for approximately 5 minutes, or
until the vegetables reach desired tenderness. Drain vegetables and add to soy
beans. In a skillet, heat oil and sauté minced chili pepper and grated lemon zest
for 1 minute. Add brown sugar, vinegar and soy sauce. Stir to combine. Remove
from heat and stir in cooked vegetables and soy beans, along with cubed tofu,
cantaloupe, celery and lemon juice. Stir until ingredients are well coated and serve.

NUTRITIONAL VALUES

Protein %	29.00
Carbohydrates %	40.00
Fat %	31.00

Protein (g)	32.00	*Saturated Fat (g)*	1.00
Carbohydrates (g)	44.00	*Monounsaturated Fat (g)*	2.00
Fat (g)	15.00	*Total Dietary Fiber (g)*	4.00

true taste on the go

Spicy Beef and Broccoli

approx. calories for this meal = 400

INGREDIENTS

4 oz lean eye of beef round
1 cup chopped broccoli
1 tsp chopped parsley
1/8 tsp garlic powder
1/2 tbsp soy sauce
1/8 tsp ground ginger

1 1/2 tsp peanut oil
2 tbsp water
1/4 tsp red pepper flakes
1 tbsp ketchup
1/2 tsp cornstarch

INSTRUCTIONS

Prepare rice following package instructions. Cut steak into thin slices. In a wok or skillet, heat oil over medium-high heat and stir-fry steak. When browned, remove meat and set aside. Add chopped broccoli, 1/2 the amount of water, parsley, red pepper flakes and garlic powder. Cover and cook for 5 minutes. In a small bowl, mix together ketchup, remaining water, soy sauce, cornstarch and ginger. Mix well and then add to skillet with cooked meat. Bring to a boil and cook for about 5 minutes or until the sauce thickens. Serve over cooked rice.

NUTRITIONAL VALUES

Protein %	33.00
Carbohydrates %	40.00
Fat %	27.00
Protein (g)	33.00
Carbohydrates (g)	40.00
Fat (g)	12.00
Saturated Fat (g)	1.00
Monounsaturated Fat (g)	5.00
Total Dietary Fiber (g)	8.00

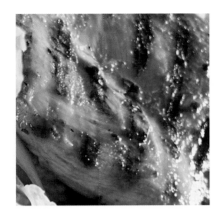

Orange Chicken Sizzler

approx. calories for this meal = 400

INGREDIENTS

1/4 cup orange juice

1/4 tsp salt

1 tsp brown sugar

3/4 tsp cornstarch

1/4 cup raw snow peas

4 oz raw boneless skinless
  chicken breast

1 tbsp soy sauce

1 tsp chopped garlic

2 tsp canola oil

1/4 cup canned bean sprouts

1/2 cup cooked medium-grain
  brown rice

INSRUCTIONS

In a bowl, combine orange juice, 1 tsp grated orange zest, soy sauce, salt, garlic and brown sugar. Mix well and set aside. In a skillet, heat oil over medium-high heat. Cut chicken into bite-size pieces and place into skillet. Stir-fry chicken until cooked through and no longer pink inside, about 7 minutes. Pour orange sauce over chicken and cook until sauce begins to bubble. Add cornstarch, a little bit at a time to thicken sauce. Add bean sprouts and snow peas and cook a few minutes more. Serve over cooked brown rice.

NUTRITIONAL VALUES

Protein %	*32.00*
Carbohydrates %	*40.00*
Fat %	*28.00*
Protein (g)	*31.00*
Carbohydrates (g)	*40.00*
Fat (g)	*12.00*
Saturated Fat (g)	*1.00*
Monounsaturated Fat (g)	*1.00*
Total Dietary Fiber (g)	*3.00*

true taste on the go

Healthy Hot Dogs with Beans

approx. calories for this meal = 400

INGREDIENTS

1 mixed-grain hamburger/hot dog bun

1 vegetarian hot dog

1/2 cup vegetarian baked beans

6 medium baby carrots

1 tbsp light ranch dip

INSTRUCTIONS

Prepare vegetarian hot dog following package instructions. Serve on bun with your choice of ketchup, mustard or relish. Add beans on top of patty. Enjoy with a side of vegetables and dairy-free dip.

NUTRITIONAL VALUES

Protein %	24.00
Carbohydrates %	46.00
Fat %	30.00
Protein (g)	22.00
Carbohydrates (g)	47.00
Fat (g)	15.00
Saturated Fat (g)	1.00
Monounsaturated Fat (g)	1.00
Total Dietary Fiber (g)	8.00

Phase 3: Maintenance Plan

Now that you have reached your weight loss goals, you will want to continue eating hormonally-balanced meals to remain lean and fit and to keep your immune system strong to help ward off future illness or disease such as heart disease, cancer or stroke. The Maintenance Plan focuses on nutrient-rich and delicious food options that will tempt all palates.

Pineapple Banana Smoothie

approx. calories for this meal = 400

INGREDIENTS

30 g protein powder
10 fl oz filtered water
3 canned pineapple rings (in water)
1/2 medium banana
1 tsp flaxseed oil
4 pieces wheat melba toast
1 oz reduced-fat mild cheddar cheese

INSTRUCTIONS

Place first 5 ingredients in a blender and blend until smooth. Enjoy with cheese and melba toast.

NUTRITIONAL VALUES

Protein %	31.00
Carbohydrates %	42.00
Fat %	27.00
Protein (g)	33.00
Carbohydrates (g)	45.00
Fat (g)	13.00
Saturated Fat (g)	6.00
Monounsaturated Fat (g)	1.00
Total Dietary Fiber (g)	2.00

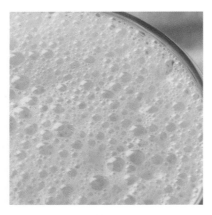

true taste on the go

High-Fiber AM Crunch
approx. calories for this meal = 300

INGREDIENTS

1/3 cup 100% bran cereal
1/2 cup skim milk
3 tsp flaxseeds
3 oz cottage cheese (1% fat)
8 raw almonds

INSTRUCTIONS

Place bran cereal and milk in a cereal bowl. Add flaxseeds and nuts. Serve with cottage cheese. Sprinkle with nuts.

NUTRITIONAL VALUES

Protein %	28.00
Carbohydrates %	43.00
Fat %	29.00
Protein (g)	22.00
Carbohydrates (g)	35.00
Fat (g)	11.00
Saturated Fat (g)	1.00
Monounsaturated Fat (g)	4.00
Total Dietary Fiber (g)	11.00

Almond Yogurt Mixed with Fruit and Granola

approx. calories for this meal = 400

INGREDIENTS

8 oz low-fat plain yogurt
1 tsp almond butter
1/2 banana
2 tbsp low-fat granola cereal
1 piece light string cheese

INSTRUCTIONS

Mix almond butter into yogurt. Add sliced banana and granola. Serve with string cheese.

NUTRITIONAL VALUES

Protein %	*26.00*
Carbohydrates %	*47.00*
Fat %	*27.00*
Protein (g)	*22.00*
Carbohydrates (g)	*49.00*
Fat (g)	*11.00*
Saturated Fat (g)	*4.00*
Monounsaturated Fat (g)	*2.00*
Total Dietary Fiber (g)	*3.00*

true taste on the go

Awesome Applesauce
Pancake Breakfast

approx. calories for this meal = 300

INGREDIENTS

1/4 cup whole-wheat pancake mix

10 g protein powder

1/2 tsp ground cinnamon

1 large omega-3 egg

2 tbsp applesauce

1/4 tsp lemon juice

2 tbsp 1% milk

1 serving cooking oil spray

1 slice of turkey bacon

INSTRUCTIONS

Combine pancake mix, protein powder and cinnamon in a large bowl. Make a
well in the center of pancake mix and add egg, applesauce, lemon juice and
milk. Stir mixture until smooth. Heat a non-stick pan over medium-high heat
and coat the pan with non-fat cooking spray. Pour batter in pan and brown
pancakes on both sides. Coat another non-stick pan with non-fat cooking spray
and cook turkey bacon. Serve pancakes with turkey bacon.

NUTRITIONAL VALUES

Protein %	*28.00*
Carbohydrates %	*45.00*
Fat %	*27.00*
Protein (g)	*21.00*
Carbohydrates (g)	*34.00*
Fat (g)	*9.00*
Saturated Fat (g)	*3.00*
Monounsaturated Fat (g)	*2.00*
Total Dietary Fiber (g)	*1.00*

Strawberry Waffle Delight

approx. calories for this meal = 300

INGREDIENTS

1 whole-grain waffle
6 oz low-fat plain yogurt
15 g protein powder
1/2 cup sliced strawberries
1 tsp maple syrup

INSTRUCTIONS

Prepare waffles following package instructions. Top with sliced strawberries, yogurt mixed with protein powder and maple syrup.

NUTRITIONAL VALUES

Protein %	*27.00*
Carbohydrates %	*47.00*
Fat %	*26.00*
Protein (g)	*23.00*
Carbohydrates (g)	*37.00*
Fat (g)	*8.00*
Saturated Fat (g)	*2.00*
Monounsaturated Fat (g)	*2.00*
Total Dietary Fiber (g)	*5.00*

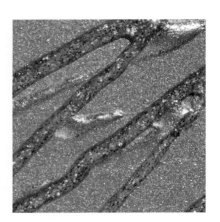

true taste on the go

Chocolate Lover's Tofu Smoothie

approx. calories for this meal = 400

INGREDIENTS

8 fl oz soymilk

6 oz soft tofu

20 g protein powder

1 tbsp unsweetened cocoa powder

2/3 small banana

INGREDIENTS

Place all ingredients in a blender and blend until smooth.

NUTRITIONAL VALUES

Protein %	*31.00*
Carbohydrates %	*43.00*
Fat %	*26.00*
Protein (g)	*31.00*
Carbohydrates (g)	*42.00*
Fat (g)	*11.00*
Saturated Fat (g)	*2.00*
Monounsaturated Fat (g)	*2.00*
Total Dietary Fiber (g)	*2.00*

Heart Healthy Garden Omelet
approx. calories for this meal = 300

INGREDIENTS

1/2 tsp extra-virgin olive oil

2 large omega-3 eggs

2 large egg whites

1/4 cup chopped raw sweet red pepper

1/4 cup canned mushroom slices

1 slice rye bread

1 large cantaloupe wedge

1 tbsp non-fat Italian salad dressing

1/4 cup chopped raw green pepper

1/4 cup chopped onion

1 tbsp non-fat cream cheese

INSTRUCTIONS

Cook dressing, mushrooms, onions and pepper in a small non-stick pan over medium heat until tender. Set aside and keep warm. Combine egg and egg whites in a bowl. Coat an omelet pan with oil and place over medium heat. Pour in egg mixture and cook until top is thickened and no visible liquid remains. Top with vegetable medley. Fold omelet in half. Serve with rye bread, cream cheese and cantaloupe wedge.

NUTRITIONAL VALUES

Protein %	30.00
Carbohydrates %	40.00
Fat %	30.00
Protein (g)	29.00
Carbohydrates (g)	39.00
Fat (g)	12.00
Saturated Fat (g)	3.00
Monounsaturated Fat (g)	4.00
Total Dietary Fiber (g)	6.00

true taste on the go

Turkish Scrambled Eggs

approx. calories for this meal = 300

INGREDIENTS

1 tbsp chopped onion

1 green chili pepper

1 large omega-3 egg

1/6 tsp salt

1/6 tsp paprika

1 red tomato

1 tsp extra-virgin olive oil

2 large egg whites

1/8 tsp ground black pepper

INSTRUCTIONS

Remove the skin from the tomato and chop. Heat oil in a pan and sauté tomato until soft and then add chopped pepper and tomato. Cook for another minute. While tomato mixture is cooking, beat the eggs with salt, pepper and paprika. Pour the egg over the vegetables and stir until the egg sets. When egg is fully cooked, serve.

NUTRITIONAL VALUES

Protein %	27.00
Carbohydrates %	43.00
Fat %	30.00
Protein (g)	18.00
Carbohydrates (g)	29.00
Fat (g)	9.00
Saturated Fat (g)	2.00
Monounsaturated Fat (g)	2.00
Total Dietary Fiber (g)	6.00

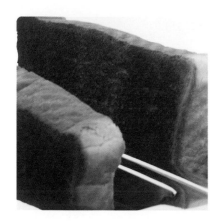

Peach French Toast

approx. calories for this meal = 400

INGREDIENTS

1/2 tsp olive oil
2 slices whole-grain bread
3 large egg whites
1 large omega-3 egg
1 tsp ground cinnamon
1 tsp powdered sugar
1/4 cup sliced raw peach
2 tsp maple syrup
2 slices turkey bacon

INSTRUCTIONS

Soak bread in beaten egg whites. Coat a non-stick pan with non-fat cooking oil spray or with a small amount of oil. Cook bread over medium heat until both sides are done. Top with cinnamon, powdered sugar, thinly sliced fruit and maple syrup. Spray non-fat cooking oil spray in a second pan. Cook turkey bacon over medium-high heat. Serve turkey bacon with French toast.

NUTRITIONAL VALUES

Protein %	27.00
Carbohydrates %	42.00
Fat %	31.00
Protein (g)	30.00
Carbohydrates (g)	45.00
Fat (g)	15.00
Saturated Fat (g)	4.00
Monounsaturated Fat (g)	2.00
Total Dietary Fiber (g)	11.00

true taste on the go

Broccoli Turkey Melt

approx. calories for this meal = 400

INGREDIENTS

1/2 cup broccoli florets
2 slices toasted whole-wheat bread
1 tbsp mustard
3 oz turkey breast
1/4 cup shredded low-fat cheddar cheese
1 side salad
1/2 cup low-fat yogurt

INSTRUCTIONS

Steam broccoli, drain and set aside. Spread mustard onto bread and place on a baking sheet. Top both slices of bread with turkey slices, broccoli and cheese. Broil in oven for about 2 minutes or until cheese is melted. Serve with a side salad (2 cups lettuce, 1/2 cup sliced cucumber, 2 tomato slices, 1 tsp olive oil, 1 tbsp balsamic vinegar). Enjoy with yogurt for dessert.

NUTRITIONAL VALUES

Protein %	32.00
Carbohydrates %	43.00
Fat %	25.00
Protein (g)	40.00
Carbohydrates (g)	54.00
Fat (g)	14.00
Saturated Fat (g)	3.00
Monounsaturated Fat (g)	1.00
Total Dietary Fiber (g)	5.00

Melted Cheese and Avocado Pita
approx. calories for this meal = 400

INGREDIENTS

2 oz shredded low-fat cheddar cheese
1/4 avocado, sliced
1/2 whole-wheat pita
2 slices red tomato
4 slices peeled cucumber
1/2 pink, red or white grapefruit

INSTRUCTIONS

Place cheese and avocado inside pita. Put in a toaster oven and bake for a few minutes or until cheese is melted. Top with tomato and cucumber. Enjoy with grapefruit on the side.

NUTRITIONAL VALUES

Protein %	29.00
Carbohydrates %	41.00
Fat %	30.00
Protein (g)	23.00
Carbohydrates (g)	34.00
Fat (g)	11.00
Saturated Fat (g)	2.00
Monounsaturated Fat (g)	2.00
Total Dietary Fiber (g)	8.00

true taste on the go

Reuben Sandwich

approx. calories for this meal = 400

INGREDIENTS

2 slices rye bread
2 oz extra-lean corned beef
1 oz mozzarella cheese
1 tbsp sauerkraut
1/2 tsp butter
1/2 medium apple

INSTRUCTIONS

Heat a non-stick pan over medium-high heat. Place corned beef, mozzarella and sauerkraut between the 2 slices of bread. Spread butter onto both outer sides of the sandwich and grill on the pan. Cook both sides until browned and cheese is melted. Enjoy with fruit.

NUTRITIONAL VALUES

Protein %	30.00
Carbohydrates %	42.00
Fat %	28.00
Protein (g)	28.00
Carbohydrates (g)	41.00
Fat (g)	12.00
Saturated Fat (g)	1.00
Monounsaturated Fat (g)	1.00
Total Dietary Fiber (g)	7.00

Black Bean and Egg Pocket

approx. calories for this meal = 400

INGREDIENTS

1 whole-wheat pita
1/2 cup canned black beans
1/4 cup organic mild or medium salsa
1 tsp chopped parsley
1 tsp olive oil
1 large omega-3 egg
2 large egg whites
1 dash table salt
1 oz shredded low-fat cheddar cheese

INSTRUCTIONS

Mix beans, salsa and parsley in a bowl. In another bowl, whisk egg, egg whites and salt. Heat oil in a non-stick pan over medium-high heat. Add egg mixture. Cover and cook for a few minutes until almost set. Sprinkle shredded cheese over top and cook for another minute until cheese is melted. Cut pita in half. Place egg in pita pockets. Top with bean mixture.

NUTRITIONAL VALUES

Protein %	32.00
Carbohydrates %	40.00
Fat %	28.00
Protein (g)	30.00
Carbohydrates (g)	39.00
Fat (g)	12.00
Saturated Fat (g)	2.00
Monounsaturated Fat (g)	3.00
Total Dietary Fiber (g)	7.00

true taste on the go

Poached Chicken Breast
with Parsley Sauce

approx. calories for this meal = 400

INGREDIENTS

3 1/2 oz raw boneless skinless chicken breast

1/8 tsp black pepper

1/4 medium lemon

1/4 cup chopped carrots

1/8 tsp sugar

1/2 tsp chopped garlic

1/4 cup parsley

1/2 cup cooked long-grain brown rice

1 tsp extra-virgin olive oil

1/2 tsp dried bay leaves

2 tbsp diced celery

1/4 cup chopped onion

1/4 cup white table wine

1 raw spring onion

2 tbsp light half-and-half sour cream

1/4 tsp lemon juice

1/2 serving soy nuts

INSTRUCTIONS

Combine oil, bay leaf, pepper, celery, lemon pieces, onion and carrot in a sauce-pan. Add enough water to fill the pan 2/3 full. Bring to a boil and simmer for 10 minutes. Add chicken and cook for 8 to 10 minutes or until chicken is no longer pink inside and juices run clear. For sauce combine white wine, sugar, onions and garlic in a small saucepan. Bring to a boil and reduce to about 1 cup. Add cream, turn off the heat and transfer the mixture into the blender. Add parsley and lemon juice and purée until smooth. Add salt and pepper to taste. Serve chicken with rice.

NUTRITIONAL VALUES

Protein %	31.00		
Carbohydrates %	41.00		
Fat %	28.00		
Protein (g)	28.00	*Saturated Fat (g)*	3.00
Carbohydrates (g)	37.00	*Monounsaturated Fat (g)*	1.00
Fat (g)	10.00	*Total Dietary Fiber (g)*	5.00

Sesame Chicken Wrap

approx. calories for this meal = 400

INGREDIENTS

1 medium whole-wheat tortilla wrap
4 oz grilled chicken breast
3 tbsp low-fat mayonnaise
1/2 tbsp soy sauce
1/2 tbsp roasted and toasted whole sesame seeds
1/4 cup Chinese pea pods
1/4 cup chopped raw sweet red pepper
1/4 cup grated carrots
2 tsp chopped almonds

INSTRUCTIONS

Grill chicken breast and cut into cubes. In a large bowl, mix mayonnaise, soy sauce and sesame seeds. Add chicken, pea pods, red pepper and almonds. Mix all ingredients well. Place mixture in center of tortilla. Top with shredded carrots. Roll up and enjoy.

NUTRITIONAL VALUES

Protein %	*30.00*
Carbohydrates %	*40.00*
Fat %	*30.00*
Protein (g)	*29.00*
Carbohydrates (g)	*41.00*
Fat (g)	*14.00*
Saturated Fat (g)	*1.00*
Monounsaturated Fat (g)	*4.00*
Total Dietary Fiber (g)	*4.00*

true taste on the go

Thai Chicken Lettuce Wraps

approx. calories for this meal = 400

INGREDIENTS

4 large iceberg lettuce leaves

2/3 cup chopped raw red cabbage

2/3 cup grated carrots

1 medium raw spring onion or scallions

1/6 avocado

2/3 cup canned bean sprouts

3 oz grilled chicken breast

1/4 cup Thai peanut sauce

INSTRUCTIONS

Place lettuce shells, shredded cabbage, carrots, onions, avocado and bean sprouts on a plate. Cut grilled chicken breast into thin strips. Take each lettuce leaf and fill with chicken, toppings and sauce.

NUTRITIONAL VALUES

Protein %	27.00
Carbohydrates %	43.00
Fat %	30.00
Protein (g)	28.00
Carbohydrates (g)	41.00
Fat (g)	13.00
Saturated Fat (g)	2.00
Monounsaturated Fat (g)	3.00
Total Dietary Fiber (g)	13.00

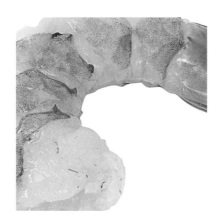

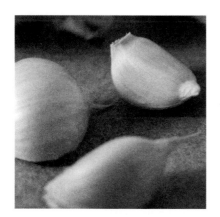

Greek Shrimp Scampi
approx. calories for this meal = 400

INGREDIENTS

1/4 lb raw shrimp
1 tsp minced garlic
1/2 cup canned chopped tomatoes
1 1/2 tsp olive oil
1/4 raw peeled lemon
1 tsp dill weed
2 tbsp feta cheese
1/2 cup cooked medium-grain brown rice
1 cup steamed chopped broccoli

INSTRUCTIONS

Shell and de-vein the shrimp, if needed, and rinse them and set aside. In a non-stick saucepan over medium heat, sauté the garlic in oil briefly and add shrimp. Cook for a minute. Add the chopped tomatoes, feta, lemon juice and dill. Stir. Add salt and pepper to taste. When the shrimp is pink and tomatoes and feta have made a sauce, remove and pour over cooked brown rice. Serve with steamed broccoli.

NUTRITIONAL VALUES

Protein %	*33.00*
Carbohydrates %	*38.00*
Fat %	*29.00*
Protein (g)	*35.00*
Carbohydrates (g)	*38.00*
Fat (g)	*14.00*
Saturated Fat (g)	*3.00*
Monounsaturated Fat (g)	*1.00*
Total Dietary Fiber (g)	*8.00*

true taste on the go

Indian Spicy Prawns

approx. calories for this meal = 400

INGREDIENTS

1/4 tsp chopped garlic

1/4 tsp cumin seed

1/4 tsp ground turmeric

1/2 tbsp olive oil

1/4 lb raw shrimp

1 dash table salt

1/4 cup sliced mango

1/4 tsp red chili pepper

1/4 tsp yellow mustard seed

2 tsp cider vinegar

1/8 cup sliced raw onion

1 tbsp water

3/4 cup cooked brown basmati rice

INSTRUCTIONS

Prepare basmati rice following package instructions. In a food processor, grind garlic, chili, cumin seed, mustard seeds and turmeric with 1 tsp of vinegar. Next, grind onion in food processor to a paste. Heat oil in pan over low heat and add onion paste until lightly brown. Add ground spices and sauté mixture until it turns reddish. Peel and de-vein shrimp and add to pan. Cook, stirring often, for about 5 minutes. Add the remaining vinegar, water and salt and simmer, uncovered, for a few more minutes. Serve over cooked basmati rice. Enjoy with mango for dessert.

NUTRITIONAL VALUES

Protein %	*28.00*
Carbohydrates %	*43.00*
Fat %	*29.00*
Protein (g)	*28.00*
Carbohydrates (g)	*43.00*
Fat (g)	*13.00*
Saturated Fat (g)	*0.00*
Monounsaturated Fat (g)	*0.00*
Total Dietary Fiber (g)	*1.00*

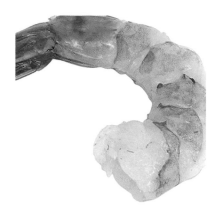

Singapore Noodles with Shrimp
approx. calories for this meal = 400

INGREDIENTS

3 tbsp chicken broth
1/4 tbsp curry powder
1 1/4 tsp peanut oil
1/4 tsp minced garlic
1 tbsp chopped onion
1/4 cup frozen peas
2/3 cup cooked rice noodles

1/4 tbsp soy sauce
1/4 tsp sugar
4 oz raw shrimp
1/2 tsp ginger root
2 tbsp chopped raw sweet red pepper
1/2 raw spring onion
1 1/2 tbsp dry-roasted cashews

INSTRUCTIONS

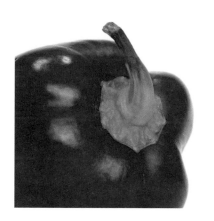

In a bowl, combine broth, soy sauce, curry powder and sugar and set aside. In a non-stick pan, heat 1/4 of oil over high heat, add shrimp and cook until pink. Remove from pan and set aside. Heat the remaining oil in the pan and stir-fry garlic and ginger for 10 seconds. Add peas, onions, pepper and chopped green onions. Stir-fry until they are crisp-tender. Stir in the curry sauce. Add the noodles and the shrimp. Cook until shrimp are done and the liquid is evaporated. Sprinkle with chopped nuts and serve.

NUTRITIONAL VALUES

Protein %	*28.00*
Carbohydrates %	*42.00*
Fat %	*30.00*
Protein (g)	*27.00*
Carbohydrates (g)	*42.00*
Fat (g)	*13.00*
Saturated Fat (g)	*2.00*
Monounsaturated Fat (g)	*4.00*
Total Dietary Fiber (g)	*3.00*

true taste on the go

Sizzling Pineapple Chicken

approx. calories for this meal = 400

INGREDIENTS

1 tsp olive oil

4 oz raw boneless skinless chicken breast

1 tbsp brown sugar

1/2 tbsp cornstarch

1 tbsp cider vinegar

1 tsp soy sauce

1/2 cup crushed pineapple (in juice)

1/4 cup sliced raw sweet red pepper

1/4 cup sliced raw onion

1 serving tossed side salad

INSTRUCTIONS

In a bowl, mix brown sugar and cornstarch. Stir in vinegar and soy sauce. Add pineapple chunks, thinly sliced red pepper and sliced onion. Set aside. Heat oil in a non-stick skillet or wok. Add sliced chicken and stir-fry until tender and meat is no longer pink inside. Add vegetable/pineapple mixture, stir until well blended. Cover and simmer over low heat for 10 minutes. Serve with a side salad (2 cups lettuce, 1/2 cup sliced cucumber, 2 slices of tomato, 1 tbsp balsamic vinegar, 1 tsp olive oil).

NUTRITIONAL VALUES

Protein %	*28.00*		
Carbohydrates %	*43.00*		
Fat %	*29.00*		
Protein (g)	*28.00*	*Saturated Fat (g)*	*1.00*
Carbohydrates (g)	*44.00*	*Monounsaturated Fat (g)*	*0.00*
Fat (g)	*13.00*	*Total Dietary Fiber (g)*	*3.00*

Dinner Pizza Omelet

approx. calories for this meal = 400

INGREDIENTS

1 large omega-3 egg

1/2 tbsp water

1 dash table salt

1 raw spring onion

1/6 tsp dried basil

1/6 tsp dried rosemary

1 slice rye bread

1 large egg white

1 serving olive oil cooking spray

1 dash ground black pepper

4 slices red tomato

1/6 tsp dried oregano

1 oz mozzarella cheese

1 cup grapes

INSTRUCTIONS

Preheat oven on broil. In a bowl, whisk together eggs, water, salt and pepper. Slice onions and tomato. Coat a non-stick pan with cooking oil spray (make sure pan is oven-safe). Add egg mixture, gently stirring until most of the eggs are set. Turn off heat and add the topping to the egg, onions, tomato, herbs and shredded cheese. Place the pan in the oven until cheese browns and eggs are fully set. Enjoy with bread and fruit.

NUTRITIONAL VALUES

Protein %	*27.00*
Carbohydrates %	*45.00*
Fat %	*28.00*
Protein (g)	*27.00*
Carbohydrates (g)	*46.00*
Fat (g)	*11.00*
Saturated Fat (g)	*1.00*
Monounsaturated Fat (g)	*2.00*
Total Dietary Fiber (g)	*4.00*

true taste on the go

Pesto Chicken Spinach Wrap

approx. calories for this meal = 400

INGREDIENTS

1 1/2 tbsp pesto sauce with basil
2 tsp red wine vinegar
4 oz raw boneless skinless chicken breast
1/2 small raw sweet red pepper
1 medium spinach tortilla wrap
2 tbsp shredded non-fat mozzarella cheese
1 lettuce leaf
1 cup strawberry halves
3/4 cup blueberries

INSTRUCTIONS

Mix 1/3 amount of pesto and vinegar in a bowl and add salt and pepper to taste. Add chicken and turn to coat. Cover and refrigerate for at least 30 minutes. Remove chicken from marinade. Grill chicken over medium-high flame, about 4 minutes per side, until chicken is no longer pink inside. Grill red pepper skin side down, about 5 minutes until skin is charred. Let cool for a few minutes and remove skin. Cut chicken and red pepper into strips. Spread remaining pesto sauce on tortilla. Top with chicken, peppers, cheese and lettuce. Roll up and enjoy with mixed fruit for dessert.

NUTRITIONAL VALUES

Protein %	30.00		
Carbohydrates %	40.00		
Fat %	30.00		
Protein (g)	36.00	*Saturated Fat (g)*	3.00
Carbohydrates (g)	49.00	*Monounsaturated Fat (g)*	1.00
Fat (g)	17.00	*Total Dietary Fiber (g)*	8.00

Appendix A:
Glycemic Tables

GLYCEMIC INDEX AND GLYCEMIC LOAD

Please note that the numbers below have been compiled from a wide array of research studies. These numbers may vary slightly from other lists you may find.

FRUITS AND FRUIT PRODUCTS

Food Item	Glycemic Index (GI) (Low < 55)	Serving Size (g)	Glycemic Load (GL) (Low < 10)
Apples, raw	34	120	5
Apple juice, unsweetened	41	250	11
Apricots	57	120	5
Apricots, dried	32	60	8
Banana, ripe	51	120	13
Banana, underripe	30	120	6
Banana, overripe	40	120	12
Cherries	22	120	3
Cranberry juice	68	250	24
Dates, dried	103	60	42
Figs, dried	61	60	16
Grapefruit	25	120	3
Grapefruit juice, unsweetened	48	250	9
Grapes	46	120	8
Grapes, black	59	120	11
Kiwi	53	120	6
Lychee, canned in syrup	79	120	16
Mango	51	120	8
Marmalade, orange	48	30	9
Orange	42	120	5
Orange juice	52	250	12
Papaya	59	120	10
Peach	42	120	5
Peach, in heavy syrup	58	120	9
Pear	38	120	4
Pear halves, in syrup	25	120	4
Pineapple	59	120	7

Plum	39	120	5
Prunes, pitted	29	60	10
Raisins	64	60	28
Cantaloupe	65	120	4
Strawberries, fresh	40	120	1
Strawberry jam	51	30	10
Sultanas	56	60	25
Tomato juice, no sugar added	38	250	4
Watermelon	72	120	4

VEGETABLES

Food Item	Glycemic Index (GI) (Low < 55)	Serving Size (g)	Glycemic Load (GL) (Low < 10)
Broad beans	79	80	9
Green peas	48	80	3
Pumpkin	75	80	3
Sweet corn	54	80	9
Beet root	64	80	5
Carrots	71	80	3
Cassava, boiled	46	100	12
Parsnips	97	80	12
Baked potato	85	150	26
French fries, frozen	75	150	22
Instant mashed potato	85	150	17
New potato	57	150	17
Sweet potato	61	150	17

LEGUMES AND NUTS

Food Item	Glycemic Index (GI) (Low < 55)	Serving Size (g)	Glycemic Load (GL) (Low < 10)
Black eye beans, boiled	42	150	13
Chick peas, boiled	28	150	8
Navy beans	38	150	12
Kidney beans, boiled	28	150	7
Black beans, cooked	20	150	5
Lentils, green, boiled	30	150	5
Lentils, red, dried	26	150	5

Food Item	Glycemic Index (GI) (Low < 55)	Serving Size (g)	Glycemic Load (GL) (Low < 10)
Lima beans, frozen	32	150	5
Mung beans, cooked	42	150	7
Peas, dried, boiled	22	150	2
Pinto beans, dried	39	150	10
Romano beans	46	150	8
Soya beans, boiled	15	150	1
Split peas, boiled	32	150	6

BREADS

Food Item	Glycemic Index (GI) (Low < 55)	Serving Size (g)	Glycemic Load (GL) (Low < 10)
Bagel, white, frozen	72	70	25
Baguette, white, plain	95	30	15
French baguette with chocolate spread	72	70	27
French baguette with butter and strawberry jam	62	70	26
Coarse barley kernel bread	27	30	5
Buckwheat bread	47	30	10
Hamburger bun	61	30	9
Kaiser roll	73	30	12
Gluten-free, multi-grain bread	79	30	10
Pumpernickel bread	46	30	5
Light rye	68	30	10
White spelt wheat bread	74	30	17
Spelt multi-grain bread	54	30	7
White flour	70	30	10
100% whole-grain bread	51	30	7
White bread	71	30	9
Kamut bread	57	30	57
Whole-wheat tortilla	30	30	6
Ryvita crispbread	63	25	10
Ryvita rye crispbread	69	25	11
Melba toast	70	30	15

PASTA AND RICE

Food Item	Glycemic Index (GI) (Low < 55)	Serving Size (g)	Glycemic Load (GL) (Low < 10)
Fettuccine, egg	32	180	15
Gluten-free pasta, maize	54	180	22
Gnocchi	68	180	33
Linguine, thick durum wheat, white	43	180	21
Macaroni and cheese, boxed (Kraft)	64	180	32
Rice noodles, dried, boiled	61	180	23
Rice pasta, brown, boiled	92	180	35
Spaghetti, protein-enriched	27	180	14
Spaghetti, white, boiled	34	180	16
Spaghetti, whole-wheat	37	180	16
Udon noodles	62	180	30
Brown rice, boiled	66	150	21
White rice, boiled	72	150	30

BREAKFAST CEREALS

Food Item	Glycemic Index (GI) (Low < 55)	Serving Size (g)	Glycemic Load (GL) (Low < 10)
All Bran™	30	30	4
Bran Chex™	58	30	4
Cheerios™	74	30	15
Corn Bran™	75	30	15
Cornflakes™ (Kellogg's)	92	30	24
Corn Pops™ (Kellogg's)	80	30	21
Cream of Wheat™ (Nabisco)	66	250	17
Crispix™ (Kellogg's)	87	30	22
Froot Loops™ (Kellogg's)	69	30	18
Frosted Flakes™ (Kellogg's)	55	30	15
Grapenuts™ (Kraft)	92	30	24
Just Right™ (Kellogg's)	60	30	13
Mini Wheats™ (Kellogg's)	72	30	15
Muesli	60	30	11
Oat Bran, raw	59	10	3
Porridge	69	250	16
Rice Krispies™ (Kellogg's)	82	30	21

true taste on the go

	Glycemic Index (GI)	Serving Size (g)	Glycemic Load (GL)
Shredded Wheat™ (Nabisco)	83	30	17
Special K™ (Kellogg's)	69	30	14

MISCELLANEOUS

Food Item	Glycemic Index (GI) (Low < 55)	Serving Size (g)	Glycemic Load (GL) (Low < 10)
Popcorn, plain	72	20	8
Honey	87	25	18

Appendix B:
Serving Sizes

CARBOHYDRATES

Fruit

1 serving of fruit = 1/2 cup or 1 small fruit
= 10 grams of carbohydrates

Vegetables

1 serving of vegetables = 1 cup
= 5 grams of carbohydrates

Beans

1 serving of beans = 1/2 cup
= 20 to 25 grams of carbohydrates

Whole Grains

1 whole-wheat tortilla = 12 grams of carbohydrates
2 pieces of crispbread = 15 grams of carbohydrates
1 slice of whole-wheat bread = 15 grams of carbohydrates
1 whole-wheat bagel = 25 to 40 grams of carbohydrates

PROTEIN

The palm of your hand without thumb or fingers or a deck
of cards = 3 ounces of protein
1 scoop of protein powder = 25 grams of protein
4 ounces of chicken, fish = 28 grams of protein
3 ounces of sirloin steak = 25 grams of protein
1/2 cup of egg whites = 13 grams of protein
1 ounce of low-fat cheese = 7 grams of protein
1 cup of lima beans = 15 grams of protein
4 ounces of firm tofu = 10 grams of protein

FAT

1 tsp of extra virgin olive oil = 5 grams of fat
7 almonds = 5 grams of fat
1/8 of an avocado = 5 grams of fat
1 tsp of peanut butter = 5 grams of fat

Appendix C:
Truestar Weight Loss Plans

The Truestar approach to weight loss has been created on the platform that everyone is different and therefore has different weight loss needs and goals. Metabolic rates, physical activity, gender, dietary likes and dislikes, current health status, previous medical conditions and dieting attempts all influence future weight loss success. Due to these influences, Truestar has developed a 3-phase approach to weight loss that will fit the needs of everyone wishing to lose weight and keep it off. For example, if you want to lose weight quickly (e.g. on average, 2 to 6 pounds or more per week)*, *Phase 1 – Metabolic Booster Plan,* with a higher protein content may be more appropriate for you. If gradual weight loss is more appealing, Phase 2 is the place to begin. To top it off, once the weight has been lost, Truestar offers a variety of maintenance plans that contain hundreds of delicious recipes and meal options so you can eat delicious foods and keep the weight off for life! The Truestar phase-based programs are:

PHASE 1 - METABOLIC BOOSTER PLAN (average weight loss is approximately 2 to 6 pounds per week)*

PHASE 2 - CONTINUUM WEIGHT LOSS PLAN (average weight loss is approximately 2 pounds per week)*

PHASE 3 – MAINTENANCE PLAN*

*Based on following the Truestar Program. Weight loss can vary per individual. Persons with certain medical conditions (e.g. thyroid condition) may lose weight at slower rates and should consult their doctor if weight loss results are not achieved.

PHASE 1 – METABOLIC BOOSTER PLAN

The Metabolic Booster Plan is suitable for those who wish to lose weight in a quick, safe and easy manner. On average, in the first 4 to 6 weeks, you can expect to lose a minimum of 2 to 6 pounds or more per week.* In subsequent weeks, an average weight loss of 1 to 2 pounds per week is normal.* This plan is best suited for people who have trouble with blood sugar control, have a slow metabolism and/or are chronic dieters with difficulty losing weight. For example, individuals who have been diagnosed with type 2 diabetes, insulin resistance, hypoglycemia (low blood sugar), high blood pressure, high cholesterol, obesity and heart disease would do best on this plan.

For optimal weight loss results and to permanently rev-up your metabolism, it is best to stay on the Metabolic Booster Plan for a minimum of 6 weeks. For certain conditions such as type 2 diabetes and hypoglycemia, the Metabolic Booster Plan is appropriate for long-term usage. If you experience weight gain when switching over to Phase 2 (the Continuum Weight Loss Plan), it is likely that your blood sugar response is not yet under control and you are still secreting too much insulin that will trigger the storage of fat. To continue to regulate and boost your metabolism, simply return to Phase 1, the Metabolic Booster Plan for 4 to 6 weeks.

*Based on following the Truestar Program. Weight loss can vary per individual. Persons with certain medical conditions (e.g. thyroid condition) may lose weight at slower rates and should consult their doctor if weight loss results are not achieved.

What foods can I eat on the Metabolic Booster Plan?

All meal plans that are available in the Metabolic Booster Plan contain the following ratio:

40% lean protein
30% low glycemic index carbohydrates
30% essential fat

It is important to eat in this ratio for each and every meal and snack in order to lose your desired weight. The protein is slightly higher in the Metabolic Booster Plan in order to jump-start metabolism and shed extra fat storage. *Protein facilitates the secretion of a hormone called glucagon, which has the opposite effect of insulin.* Glucagon signals cells to release fat into the blood, therefore promoting its use. In other words, more fat is burned and more weight is lost when protein is increased. If you eat the meals outlined in this recipe book for Phase 1 you need not worry, all the meals are perfectly balanced. If you do not eat the meals in this recipe book or those found at www.truestarhealth.com, please follow the guidelines below.

CARBOHYDRATES ALLOWED:

Fruits

Apples
Apricots
Bananas (maximum 1
  small banana per day)
Cherries
Grapefruit
Oranges
Nectarines
Peaches
Pears

Vegetables

All vegetables are allowed except for white potatoes. For example:
Broccoli
Spinach
Tomatoes/Tomato Sauce
Cauliflower
Peppers
Green beans
Sweet potatoes
Squash

Plums
Prunes, pitted
Raspberries

Strawberries
Blueberries
Blackberries
Watermelon

*Please note: raisins, cranberries,
grapes, dates and fruit juices
are not allowed.*

Beans

Navy beans
Kidney beans
Black beans
Lentils
Chickpeas
Mung beans
Pinto beans
Romano beans
Soy beans
Garbanzo beans
Split peas

Mushrooms
Water chestnuts
Romaine lettuce
Radicchio
Onions
Zucchini
Cucumber
Kale
Green or red cabbage
Collard greens
Bok choy

Grains

2 pieces of crispbread
1 cup of slow-cooking oatmeal
1 medium whole-wheat tortilla wrap
(1 maximum per day)

Please note: all of the carbohydrates allowed have a low glycemic index rating.

CARBOHYDRATES NOT ALLOWED:

Fruits – grapes, raisins, cranberries, dates and fruit juice

White potatoes, white rice

Cereals, instant oatmeal

Bread (aside from 2 pieces of crispbread per day)

Pasta

Bagels, crackers or cookies

Hamburger and hotdog buns

Juice

Candy, ice cream

Granola bars

Beer, wine

*Please note: Alcohol is not allowed in the Metabolic Booster Plan
(4 to 6 weeks).*

PROTEINS ALLOWED:

Omega-3 eggs

Egg whites

Protein powder

Low-fat dairy products such as 1% or skim milk, low-fat yogurt, low-fat cottage
 cheese or cheese

Fortified soy milk, imitation soy meats or cheese, tofu, miso, veggie burgers

Fish (salmon, tuna, mackerel, cod, anchovies, sardines, halibut, sole, etc.)

Chicken breast slices, ground chicken

Turkey (slices, turkey bacon, turkey breast, ground turkey)

Lean ground beef and lean cut meats

Veal

PROTEINS NOT ALLOWED:

Full-fat cheeses
Full-fat meat products such as steaks, ribs, pork

FATS ALLOWED:

Ground flaxseeds or flaxseed oil
1/2 handful of almonds, walnuts, soy nuts or cashews
1/4 of an avocado daily
Sesame seeds
Extra-virgin olive oil, olives (black or green)
Almond oil
Avocado oil
Canola oil
Pumpkin oil
Soy bean oil
Borage oil
Fish oil supplements
Non-hydrogenated margarine
Butter sparingly

FATS NOT ALLOWED:

Deep-fried foods such as chips, French fries, etc.
Full-fat cheese
Marbled meats
Vegetable oils such as safflower, sunflower
Hydrogenated margarine
Partially hydrogenated food items (check label)

Remember to combine a selection of carbohydrates, protein and fat at each and every meal and snack.

PHASE 2 – CONTINUUM WEIGHT LOSS PLAN

The Continuum Weight Loss Plan is designed for individuals who have successfully completed the Metabolic Booster Plan and wish to include more whole grains and carbohydrates into their diet or for those who desire a more gradual weight loss approach. Once you have successfully completed Phase 1, your metabolism should be working at a faster pace and you should not gain any weight when switching to Phase 2. If you do find yourself gaining weight, simply switch back to the Metabolic Booster Plan for another 4 to 6 weeks.

In Phase 2, you can expect to lose weight at approximately 1 to 2 pounds per week. The Continuum Weight Loss Plan contains a different ratio of carbohydrates: protein: fat vs. Phase 1 (Metabolic Booster Plan). All meals and snacks in Phase 2 have the following ratio:

40% low glycemic index carbohydrates
  (10% higher than the Metabolic Booster Plan)
30% lean protein
30% essential fat

The foods that are allowed in the Continuum Weight Loss Plan are similar to the Metabolic Booster Plan, yet there is a higher percentage of carbohydrates and whole-grain items. Additionally, 4 alcoholic beverages per week are permitted.

It is advisable to stay on Phase 2 until you reach your goal weight. Once your weight loss goals have been achieved, you can eat from any of the Truestar Maintenance Meal Plans.

Please keep in mind that all of our meals are balanced precisely to normalize insulin levels. The whole grains found in our meal plans are made of rich fibers and flours such as kamut and spelt pasta or multi-grain and flaxseed bread. Once you have lost your desired weight, if you eat whole grains in moderation and in combination with the proper amounts of protein and fat, the weight you have lost should be easily maintained. By simply sticking to the Truestar meal plans or following our foods allowed vs. not allowed — your weight loss should be successful.

In a nutshell, if you eat the meals outlined in the recipe book in Phase 2, you need not worry, all the meals are perfectly balanced. If you do not eat the meals in this recipe book or those found at www.truestarhealth.com, please follow the guidelines on the following pages.

CARBOHYDRATES ALLOWED (40%)

Fruits

All fruits with the exception of dates, raisins and sugary juices.

Beans

All types of beans

Vegetables

All vegetables are allowed except for white potatoes. Sweet potatoes and squash are allowed.

Grains

2 pieces of crispbread
1 cup of slow-cooking oatmeal
1 medium-sized whole-wheat
  tortilla wrap
1/2 cup of kamut or spelt pasta
1/2 cup of brown rice
2 slices of whole-grain bread
1 cup of whole-grain cereal
  (e.g. bran)

ALCOHOL ALLOWED

4 alcoholic beverages allowed per week. Optimal choices are:

red wine
light beer

Tip: Be sure to have a selection of protein if indulging in alcoholic beverages.

CARBOHYDRATES NOT ALLOWED

All refined flours and sugars
Cereals and instant oatmeal
White pasta, white bagels, crackers or cookies
White or refined bread

Hamburger and hotdog buns
White potatoes or rice
Juice
Candy, ice cream
Granola bars

PROTEINS ALLOWED

Same as in Phase 1 – Metabolic Booster Plan

PROTEINS TO EAT MINIMALLY (ONCE PER WEEK ONLY)

Full-fat meat products such as steaks, ribs, pork

PROTEINS NOT ALLOWED

Full-fat cheeses (all cheeses such as cheddar, mozzarella and havarti should be low-fat).

FATS ALLOWED

Same as in Phase 1 – Metabolic Booster Plan

FATS NOT ALLOWED

Same as in Phase 1 – Metabolic Booster Plan

Remember, eating carbohydrates, proteins and fats separately from each other is not the key to weight loss. The solution is to match them at each and every meal and snack.

PHASE 3 – MAINTENANCE PLAN

Now that you have reached your weight loss goal, you will want to continue eating hormonally-balanced meals to remain lean and fit and to keep your immune system strong to help ward off future illness or disease such as heart disease, cancer or stroke. The Maintenance Plan focuses on nutrient-rich and delicious food options that will tempt all palates. Similar to Phase 2, the balance of each and every meal and snack contains a breakdown of:

40% low glycemic index carbohydrates
30% lean proteins
30% essential fats

There are several options available which include:

optimal wellness plans
red meat-free plans
dairy-free plans
dairy-free and wheat-free plans
gluten-free plans
nut-free plans
vegetarian plans
vegan plans

Please note: Prior to beginning any diet plan, it is best to check with your primary healthcare practitioner.

SUPPLEMENTS TO SUPPORT WEIGHT LOSS

To further complement your weight loss results, supplement needs are matched to each nutrition phase. This unique approach to lasting weight loss allows supplements to support your body completely during all 3 phases of Truestar's nutrition program.

We begin Phase 1 with TrueLEAN 3, a gentle detox to optimize the function of the liver, kidneys and digestive tract and to assist your body with "clean-up" from years of unwholesome eating habits. Also in this stage, when sugar and carbohydrates are avoided, TrueCRAVING Control is recommended to prevent cheating, stress-related eating and to aid healthy blood sugar balance. True-BASICS supports your metabolic rate in all phases. Remember, your nutritional needs are higher when you exercise and a deficiency of just one nutrient is enough to slow your metabolism down. TrueTHERMO, a thermogenic agent, stimulates the enzymes involved in breaking down fat and can also be added to any phase. However, this product should not be taken if you have high blood pressure or a heart condition.

TrueCARB Blocker reduces the absorption of carbohydrates that are gradually added into your meal plans when entering Phase 2. This is your best choice to keep insulin levels low and to prevent weight gain. When your Phase 1 detox is completed, use TrueLEAN 2 until you reach your goal weight for continued appetite control, metabolic stimulation and blood sugar/insulin balance.

You may continue the use of the weight loss products, as needed, or consider Truestar's Optimal Wellness supplement plan once you have achieved your goal weight. The Optimal Wellness supplement plan provides your basic daily nutritional needs, antioxidant protection, calcium requirements and omega-3 oils.